ADULTS CAN'T S
THE LOSE YOUR
OWN ADVENTURE® STORIES!

"My life is depressing enough as it is. I read fiction to escape it. I didn't need to be magically transported to a world where my every decision eventually ended in failure, recrimination or abject humiliation—I already live there ... Thanks for nothing, Despair."

—Lena Olsen, age 34

"I grew up reading those pick-your-own-path books. I loved feeling like a ninja, or a spy, or even a shark. So I thought for sure I'd enjoy reading Lose Your Own Adventure books. I was wrong. So very wrong."

—Daniel Thewlis, age 41

"I hope you guys get sued. I really do."

—Bill Ziccardi, age 29

AND TEACHERS
LIKE THE SERIES TOO:

"The Warren Commission clearly proved that Oswald acted alone. It hardly helps those of us in the teaching profession when yet another book comes along peddling outlandish theories—and this one, in the insidious form of a children's book. Shame on you all."

LOSE YOUR OWN ADVENTURE—
AND MAKE READING MORE FUN!

Other Books in the **Lose Your Own Adventure®** Series.

NOTE: Do you want to help us Kickstart the next planned title in the *Lose Your Own Adventure®* family? Despair is launching a Kickstarter project to help us break through *The Glass Ceiling* on September 4th, 2013. If you enjoy *Who Killed John F. Kennedy?*, please help us accelerate the production of our next destined-to-be-brilliant satirical masterpiece!

(See the last page of this book for details.)

If you want to help us, turn to the last page of this book.

If you don't, what's your problem? Seriously?

WHO KILLED JOHN F. KENNEDY?

BY DESPAIR, INC.

A PARODY FOR GROWN-UPS

ILLUSTRATED BY PAUL STRANGER

:-(

DESPAIR, INC.®

Ages 15 and up

WHO KILLED JOHN F. KENNEDY?
A Despair, Inc. Book

2nd Edition Printing

Written by Justin Sewell

With Additional Material and Editing by Michael Schaub
Original concept by Jef & Justin Sewell

Artist: Paul Stranger

WHO KILLED
JOHN F. KENNEDY?

A NOTE TO READERS:

Often in this book, you will encounter a small italicized number at the end of a sentence. This indicates that there is additional material about the topic in the Endnotes section of this book, on the page number indicated.

WARNING!!!!

Do not read this book straight through from beginning to end! These pages contain many different misfortunes you can experience as you futilely attempt to solve the mystery of who killed John F. Kennedy. From time to time as you read along, you will be asked to make a choice. Your choice may lead to further prolonged suffering and frustration, or to your final and inevitable defeat!

Your failure to solve the John F. Kennedy Murder Mystery is inevitable—but *how* you fail depends a lot on your decisions. Some leads in the case will throw you off the track; others might get you killed—or even worse!

Remember—you cannot go back! Think carefully before you make a move! One mistake can be your last, or it just might be the next in a series *leading* to your last! And remember, just like in real life, no matter how you choose, you're ultimately destined to lose!

It's been less than a month since your good friend Billy Thompson got shot in the left buttock by a pellet gun while biking home from school.

"My rear!" he screamed, as he flew off his bike.

That night as your family ate dinner, the phone rang. Billy's parents were calling for your father's help—and why shouldn't they? He's the Chief of Police in Dallas! Little did they know that secretly, your dad couldn't solve a two-piece jigsaw puzzle! He relies *completely* on your keen detective skills to solve even the city's most obvious of crimes.

As your dad began to stammer away nervously, you took the phone from him and said, "Don't worry, Dad—I'll handle this." Your mother just looked at you sympathetically and let out a weary sigh.

The next day, you went with Billy back to the scene of the crime. After carefully examining his injury, you deduced from the angle of his entrance wounds that the shot *must* have come from the old abandoned Packard house. Sure enough, once inside, you found a treasure trove of evidence—including an empty box of Colt-brand candy cigarettes, the favorite cigs of notorious school bully Slugs O'Toole. Better still, you found an empty metal tin of .22 caliber airgun pellets with greasy fingerprints all over it!

The next day at school, you offered Slugs a bottle of root beer. When he was finished drinking it—you lifted his fingerprints. A perfect match! Slugs had no choice but to confess to the shooting. Even your longtime rival in amateur investigation, that smart-mouthed know-it-all Jenni Mudd, was impressed—and her dad works for the FBI! The school paper even ran a front page story about your keen detective skills, spreading the word throughout school that crime-solving must run in your family!

If only that were true!

Go on to the next page.

All that seems like a lifetime ago. It was only minutes ago that Principal Dunn announced over the P.A. system that President Kennedy had been shot and killed by an unknown assailant—right in downtown Dallas! School was dismissed early. Most kids headed straight home, but not you. You hopped right on your bike and headed straight for Dallas Police headquarters!

The station is packed with barking reporters, stoic policemen, tearful witnesses and more than a few angry citizens yelling things like "Kill that Commie rat!"

Towering over the crowd, the burly, street-smart Sergeant Fanucci recognizes you instantly—and helps clear a path to your dad's office, saying, "Glad you're here, kid! Your pop's in *way* over his head. As usual."

"Son—what are you doing here?!" blurts your father as Fanucci leads you in. He tries to sound stern—but it's obvious he's incredibly relieved to see you. He looks terrified.

"I want to help with the investigation, Dad!" you reply. "Just tell me what you know so far."

Looking like a deer in the headlights, your father starts to stammer away. "Well, we've got this, um, you know—the guy what maybe did it, the uhhhh …"

"The *suspect?*" you offer, trying not to sound annoyed.

"The suspect, right. Lee Oswald… We think he maybe, um, you know, shot the uh, the guy who, um… The man who runs the country, the uhh …" he trails off helplessly.

"The *President?*" you offer, no longer disguising your annoyance.

Sergeant Fanucci steps in, saying, "We think this Oswald shot the President, then iced one of our guys next—Officer Tippit." He starts cracking his knuckles, "He ain't confessed to either yet, kid, but he's gonna. Believe me."

"What about *evidence*, Dad? What do you know about the shooting itself? Ballistics? The weapon? Entrance and exit wounds? Witnesses? I need details!"

Fanucci jumps in, "Kennedy was shot down in Dealey Plaza, kid—we think from the School Book Depository, where this Commie Oswald punk works. We found a 7.65 Mauser behind some books—that's a bolt-action Kraut rifle. We got shell casings. And we got an eyeball witness who—"

Suddenly, the door bursts open. It's the beautiful yet brilliant homicide detective Dr. Nera Vivalzi—and she looks madder than a wet hen!

"Now do you believe me, Chief? I told you this would happen! But you didn't listen! And now the President's blood is on our hands!"

If you decide to question the suspect, turn to page 4.

If you ask your dad what Vivalzi means, turn to page 7.

"I want to talk to the suspect, Dad," you declare, not missing a beat. "Political assassins almost always brag about their crimes. So why doesn't this Oswald?"

"He's not bragging because he's not guilty! He's been framed!" Dr. Vivalzi exclaims as she storms out of the room.

Fanucci shakes his head. "Poor Vivalzi. Always with the conspiracies. Come on, kid, let's go see Oswald."

He again leads you through the swarms of reporters and cops, every so often clapping a policeman on the shoulder or hailing a familiar newsman. He seems to know everyone! As you reach the door to the interrogation room, a balding, stocky fellow approaches Fanucci. They shake hands in a peculiar, ritualized fashion—then Fanucci turns to you.

"Okay, kid, looks like he's talkin' to FBI Agent Hosty now," Fanucci says. "Once they're done, you can take a shot at him," he chuckles, then winks, "so to speak."

He leads you into the dark room. Seated at a small wooden table is a wiry, intense-looking fellow sporting a rumpled t-shirt and a black eye. Standing next to him is a tall man with slicked-back black hair. A few homicide detectives, in their trademark white cowboy hats, keep a respectful distance from the interrogation. So, too, do a handful of grim-faced Secret Service men.

Oswald glares at the tall, nervous man nearest him, then says, "You have been at my home two or three times now, Agent Hosty, talking to my wife. I don't appreciate your coming when I was not there."

As if that wasn't strange enough, he adds, after a tactical pause, "And you never responded to my request, Agent. To the note I left for you at your FBI office last week."

The color drains from Hosty's face as Oswald breaks into a smirk. Detectives in the room shoot uncomfortable glances to Fanucci, who offers a tiny, pathetic shrug in response. The silence is defeaning.[171]

Go on to the next page.

6

Your young detective's mind reels in shock! What could this possibly mean? The Dallas FBI was already in repeated contact with the wife of the suspected assassin of President Kennedy? How could that be? And could it really be true—that Lee Harvey Oswald hand-delivered a note to the FBI just days before the assassination? And if so, what on earth did it say?

You're eager to ask questions—but now, you're not even sure who should be interrogated first!

If you ask Agent Hosty about the note, turn to page 8.

If you ask Oswald if he shot Kennedy, turn to page 10.

Though you dread the answer, you ask your father what Dr. Vivalzi means. He bites his lip with a hangdog look, unable to speak.

"I'll tell him then!" Vivalzi says with a bark. "Just two days ago we had two police officers who witnessed strange men engaged in target practice with rifles right down in Dealey Plaza! And they got away!" [172]

You immediately grasp the terrible implications. Unable to stop yourself, you yell at your father, "Dad! You had cops who saw riflemen sighting in targets right along the Presidential motorcade route two days before Kennedy's visit, and *you didn't at least change the route*?!"

After a long silence, you father whispers sheepishly, "Don't tell your mother!"

Ugh! What an idiot!

"Well, I'm not going to sit by and watch you bungle yet another investigation by pinning it all on this, this Oswald chump," Vivalzi barks. "Anybody with half a brain can tell this is a lot bigger than that, Chief! It's a conspiracy—and I'm going to use my own resources to find out who's really behind it!"

She leaves, slamming the door behind her. Your father buries his face in his hands with a groan, but Fanucci seems strangely nonplussed.

"Poor Vivalzi," he says, shaking his head. "There she goes again, running to her conspiracy kooks." His eyes drift to the clock. "Whoa! Almost forgot. I got Oswald's police lineup comin' up. We got a witness—this Helen Markham— she says she saw the guy who shot our boy, Tippit. You wanna come along and see how we do things downtown, kid?"

If you follow him to the police lineup, turn to page 11.

If you chase after Dr. Vivalzi, turn to page 12.

8

"The FBI received a note from the suspected assassin?" you ask in shock. "What did it say? It should be turned over immediately as evidence! And excuse me, Agent Hosty, but shouldn't you recuse yourself from this investigation? Your prior connection to Oswald makes you a material witness, maybe even an accessory after the fact!"

The room falls deathly quiet. Agent Hosty glares at you, but says nothing. Fanucci drapes a burly arm over your shoulder and leads you to a nearby office. Hosty follows.

"Kid, I know you're upset," Fanucci says, "but this is an FBI agent you're talking to. Let's have a little respect."

But you're just getting warmed up! You point at Hosty, barking, "Sorry, Agent Hosty, but if you don't recuse yourself immediately, I'll have to demand to speak to your superior!"

He chuckles, shrugs, then picks up a phone, dialing quickly. After a brief wait, he says, "Agent Hosty, Dallas Bureau, for Director Hoover. Thanks."

Fanucci shakes his head in warning, but you're not about to back down now. You've got the truth on your side!

Hosty continues, "Sir, I've got the Dallas police chief's son here, asking to speak with my superior. Here he is."

You take the phone and say, "Hello, Director Hoover."

"Hello yourself," says J. Edgar Hoover briskly. "Now pay attention, son. I don't know what you know, or think you know, but I've run the world's largest investigative body for longer than you've been alive. And I'm telling you now this case is open and shut. Oswald is the killer. End of story."

"Forgive my bluntness, sir, but you don't have jurisdiction here," you say. "Assassination isn't a federal crime. This is a murder case for the Dallas Police to solve."

Hoover raises his voice. "There is more at stake here than jurisdictional protocol, son. The public deserves to be satisfied that Oswald acted alone, and we shall prove—"

"The public?" you laugh. "The public deserves to know that the FBI has a lot to account for here, since your agent was in contact with the presumed assassin before the—"

"That means NOTHING!" Hoover roars back.

Go on to the next page.

After a few moments, he calmly continues, "Now, I've heard a lot about you, son. You did a crack job on that Billy Thompson pellet gun case last month. You're a natural detective."

Zowie! Sounds like Hoover's reputation for omniscience is well earned!

"Th-thank you, sir," you stammer in surprise.

"So," he continues, "if you help us build our case against Mr. Oswald, I will personally see to it that we put that sharp mind of yours to work for the good of the country. But if you continue to dirty our investigation with your erroneous, irresponsible speculations, well ... then I'm afraid you may force me to disclose evidence of some of your more deviant sexual activities with the public at large."

Sexual blackmail? What a laugh! Hoover must *really* have something to hide if he's resorting to such desperate measures. But he's obviously mistaken you for someone else—you're as pure as the driven snow. You haven't even held a girl's hand before. You've been saving that for marriage. So he couldn't possibly have any dirt on you!

If you tell Hoover you'll help make the case against Oswald, turn to page 16.

If you tell Hoover you're going to tell the press about FBI foreknowledge, turn to page 18.

You turn to Lee Harvey Oswald and ask, "Did you kill the President?"

"No," he replies, "I've not been charged with that. In fact, nobody has said that to me yet. I did not do it—I didn't shoot anyone. I'm still waiting for someone to come forward to give me legal assistance."

"Wait a minute," you say to Oswald in surprise. "You don't even have a lawyer yet?"

He shakes his head, clearly annoyed.

You turn to Sergeant Fanucci. "We can't interrogate a suspect who has been denied legal representation. That's a Constitutional right."

Oswald chimes in again, his irritation obvious, "As I've said, I'd like to be represented by Mr. John Abt with the ACLU. I don't know him personally, but—" *171*

"But if he's good enough to represent the Communist Party of the USA, he's good enough for you, right?" Fanucci says, to a chorus of bitter chuckles.

Suddenly, the door opens. Oswald is led out of the room, surrounded by several officers. As he enters the hallway, reporters start barking out questions.

"What's going on?" you ask Fanucci.

"It's time for his lineup—with a witness who saw him shoot our guy J.D. Tippit. Don't worry, kid, this won't take long," he replies, leading you out of the room.

Go on to the next page.

Sergeant Fanucci leads you to a dark room in the basement with a large, one-way screen set up in the far wall. A few cops are here, gathered around a TV set, watching the news. But one younger officer stands nearby, talking with a dark-haired, terrified-looking middle-aged woman who must surely be the witness. Ugh—she reeks of ammonia!

The officer addresses her gently, "Just to confirm, Mrs. Markham. You're on the record as describing the man who shot Officer Tippit as being short, stocky, and bushy-haired—with a ruddy complexion, correct?"

"Yes, that's right, yes!" she says, bursting into tears.

On the other side of the screen, a door opens. A line of four men enter the room. The first, third, and last man in the line are each clean-cut and well-dressed. But Oswald, in the second position, is a dishevelled wreck. He sports a fresh shiner over an eye, abrasions on his face, and a wrinkled white t-shirt. He's even cuffed to the men on either side!

Turn to page 14.

You run out into the hallway, but there's no sign of Dr. Vivalzi. It's just another endless sea of cops and reporters in all directions.

But down a distant hallway, you hear a man cry out in a loud catcall, *"Rowwwwwwr!"*

You spring into action, pushing through the crowds. Sure enough, you catch a glimpse of Vivalzi's lustrous head of black hair, just as she exits the building. You duck and weave your way through the masses, desperate to catch up. Finally, you reach the exit and sprint out into the street.

She's already in her car, backing out to leave. You rush towards her, sweaty and out of breath, gasping, "Dr. Vivalzi, where are you going? I want to help!"

She rolls down her window, eyeing you skeptically, then says, "You? The police chief's son? You want to help me?"

"Absolutely!" you reply. "If what you're saying about the rehearsed assassination is true, then there's no way Oswald could've acted alone. If he acted at all."

She nods, but still looks a bit skeptical. Finally, she opens the passenger door, and says, "All right, then. But I'm warning you in advance. You're putting your life in danger by joining us, and—"

"Us?" you interrupt. "Who else is—"

"You'll see soon enough," she answers.

She begins to drive, dialing her radio to KLIF-AM. The news host speaks soberly, "—there was absolutely no warning that this would take place. Of course, these things always come so spontaneously. Should there be any warning then the president would be better protected and an alternate route could be prepared, but everything had gone smoothly—"

"Unbelievable!" she shouts, turning off the radio in disgust. "Your father just ..."

She stops in mid-sentence, her eyes growing narrow and suspicious. She then reaches under her seat, pulls out a blindfold, and hands it to you.

"Put this blindfold on," she says. "Otherwise, I can't bring you with me. We can't afford to have our hideout penetrated—especially not now."

If you refuse to put on the blindfold, turn to page 23.

If you put on the blindfold, turn to page 22.

14

Mrs. Markham, shaking violently, is unable to speak. The young officer places a gentle arm over her shoulder and says, "It's OK. They can't see you. Just tell me if you recognize the man that you saw shoot Officer Tippit."

She stares at the line-up for several seconds, then shakes her head, crying even harder. Sergeant Fanucci looks over towards the television set and breaks into his strange smile, "Well, well. Looky there ..."

On the TV, news footage shows the rumpled suspect being led through the halls by police. Mrs. Marhkam watches and listens as the suspect is identified. Then she turns and through teary eyes points unsteadily at Suspect #2.

The young officer writes in his clipboard. "Let the record show that Mrs. Helen Markham has identified one Lee Harvey Oswald as the shooter of Officer Tippit," he says.

You can't believe what's happening! This is an obvious farce—they might as well have hung a sign over his neck reading "THE KILLER"! [171]

If you complain to Fanucci about leading the witness,
turn to page 30.

If you choose to say nothing, turn to page 31.

"Well, Director Hoover," you reply, "if you're absolutely sure you've got your man with Oswald, I guess I'll help you in any way that I can."

"Capital!" he replies. "You're just the kind of person we need in the FBI. I want you to go home for now, let us clean up this mess. We'll call you the second we need you."

You want to protest, but a deal's a deal.

"All right, Director," you say, "I'll wait for your call."

You bike back to your house unhappily, still troubled by what you'd witnessed at the station.

Your mother looks surprised to see you home. "What happened, son? Did you learn anything?"

"Looks like Oswald did it, Mom," you reply quietly. "Pretty open and shut. Even Dad can solve this one."

You hate not being straight with her, but you know she'd be disappointed if she knew you'd backed down on a provocative lead. And surely, when Oswald's trial happens, all of these details—his prior FBI contact, the target practice, whatever else—will all come out, right?

You and your mother sit glued to the TV, taking in every detail about the assassination. But Friday night passes with no calls from the FBI. As does Saturday. By Sunday morning, you wonder if you've made a mistake, or if Hoover was lying to you about making you a part of his team.

As you both sit watching the flag-draped coffin being led down Pennsylvania Avenue to the Capitol rotunda to lie in state, the broadcast is suddenly interrupted with live footage from Dallas. Oswald is about to be transferred in an armored car to the county jail, and is cuffed to a man in a cowboy hat you recognize as James Leavelle, homicide detective.

As they walk through the basement, suddenly a man in a grey hat leaps out from the crowd, and shoots Oswald right in the gut! Oswald cries out in pain—and total chaos ensues! Your mom screams in shock, hand on her mouth.

Just then, the phone rings. Your mother goes to answer it, and after only a few moments, she turns to you, even more shocked.

Go on to the next page.

"It's FBI Director Hoover," she says, mystified. "He wants to speak with you?"

You can't believe it—you'd think he'd have better things to do right now!

"Hello?" you whisper.

The now-familiar voice begins somberly, "It's tragic what just took place in Dallas. But maybe it's for the best. At least it spares the nation the ordeal of some endless trial."

"But if he's alive...?"

"My understanding is that his wounds are fatal."

This is just too much! You know a cover-up when you see one! Now you KNOW something criminal is taking place. And the FBI is leading the charge!

"On a happier note," Hoover continues, suddenly gay, "Someone here pulled a boner and I have a new opening— for a Junior Detective in Dallas. And for your help in this time of dire crisis, I'm happy to extend the invitation."

Ugh! What a dilemma! A chance to be real investigator sounds exciting, but as a reward for your silence, it seems tainted!

If you take Hoover's offer, turn to page 38.

If you decline it, turn to page 36.

"I'm sorry, Director Hoover, but I'm calling your bluff," you reply, "The American people deserve the truth. If you don't have the guts to tell it to them, then I'll do it myself!"

"Suit yourself," Hoover says flatly and hangs up.

Hopping on your bike, you pedal towards the downtown offices of the Dallas Morning News. On the faces of Dallasites you pass, you see shock, grief, and a shared sense of shame.

Once you reach the news building, you jump off your bike and storm into the newsroom. The place is abuzz with quick-talking reporters and clattering typewriters. History, however terrible, was just made in Dallas—and this paper has a front-row seat. You can hardly wait to share your story.

But no sooner have you entered the news floor than you're grabbed by the neck by a security guard, who drags you towards the exit.

"What are you doing? I've got breaking news about the assassination! I've got to talk to someone!" you plead.

"We don't want your kind here, nancy! Now get out—and stay out!" he growls as he shoves you out the door.

You hit the pavement with a thud. Obviously, Hoover must have contacts at the paper. But you're not giving up so fast! If the Morning News won't publish the story, you'll break it yourself in the school paper! After all, your friend Billy Thompson is the editor—and he owes you a favor!

You call Billy up and tell him your amazing story. He can hardly believe his ears.

"What a scoop! This'll be on the front page, above the fold!" he says excitedly. "Write it up this weekend and meet me Monday morning in the journalism room. We can set type on it and have this printing by lunch!"

You sit at the typewriter and bang out your headline: "EXCLUSIVE—FBI HAD PRIOR CONTACT WITH SUSPECTED ASSASSIN LEE HARVEY OSWALD!"

You spend Saturday working on your story—recreating the interrogation scene you'd witnessed Friday in crisp, vivid detail. But by Sunday morning, the detective inside you is longing to return to headquarters to continue investigating.

"Oh, well," you ask yourself with a chuckle. "How much could Dad screw up between now and Monday?"

As you turn on the TV to check the news, you have your answer. Oswald was gunned down moments ago at the police station by a local nightclub owner named Jack Ruby! You notice, to your shock, he's the very same man you saw shaking hands with Fanucci outside the interrogation room! Oswald's murderer was a friend of the Dallas police?

"You can take a shot at him—so to speak ..." Fanucci had said. But was he really talking to you? Or were the Dallas police letting Ruby know he could kill Oswald with their blessing? And where was the FBI in all this? As the questions flood your mind, the phone rings. It's Billy.

"They killed him—right on TV!" he exclaims. "Jeepers! I can't believe it! What do we do?"

"What do we *do*?" you reply, not missing a beat. "We meet at school tomorrow and break the story of the year!"

That's your plan, anyway...

Turn to page 20.

Monday morning you arrive at school. You're ready to get to work, just as soon as you stop by your locker. But something's wrong. It's been papered over with photos. You grab one. It's a close-up shot of you, examining Billy's pellet gun wound to the butt cheek out at the Packard place!

Oh, no! People might think you're a—

"Hey there, Inspector Rectum," growls a menacing voice from behind.

You spin around to see the notorious school bully Slugs O'Toole towering over you! The freckle-faced terror slams you against your locker with one of his massive fists. Over his shoulder, you see Butch, one of his henchmen in the Tiger gang. He's giving Billy an atomic wedgie!

"Wait, Slugs, I can explain!" you stammer, trying to maintain your composure, "It's not what it looks like!"

A crowd has begun to form in the hall. The very same kids who only weeks ago had hailed you as a hero for your detective work on Billy's shooting are now laughing and jeering at you. Someone begins to chant, "Fight fight fight!"—and soon, the entire crowd has joined the chorus.

"There's nothing to explain, Detective. I can see that you cracked the case of Billy's butt wide open!" Slugs says, to howls of laughter. "Now I'm doing the same to your face!"

And before you can even get another word out, he throws his first punch—a lightning-fast hook that has you seeing stars! Again and again, his punches rain down, knocking you to the floor, where even more photos have spilled from your locker. Behind you, a terrified Billy Thompson is being pounded like a rented mule!

Watching the chaos just yards away is your old rival Jenni Mudd, her ever-trusty camera around her neck. She took those misleading photos—there's no doubt about it. But why? Was she just trying to put your rival agency out of work? Was she really working for the FBI all along? Or both?

You have a lot of time to ponder that—seeing that you'll be in traction for a year. The doctors say there's even a chance you might walk again. If you're lucky.

YOU LOSE

You slip on the blindfold.

"Thanks," she says, calming down. "Sorry for the precautions, but the Altair Society can't afford to take chances. Especially not now."

"The Altair Society? What's that?" you ask.

"We're an elite band of researchers," she says. "Our mission is to expose corruption and conspiracy wherever we find it. But we've made powerful enemies, even inside the U.S. government. They'd love nothing more than to infiltrate and destroy us! So we meet in secret. And today we start our most important mission—one we'd feared was coming. Today we start searching for who *really* killed JFK!"

You're immediately intrigued. Elite researchers may be just what this case needs! Given what you heard about men engaged in target practice in Dealey Plaza, it was obviously a conspiracy. Only a fool could think otherwise. And if this Altair Society actually anticipated the attack, then they may already have a good guess as to who really killed JFK.

The car comes to a stop. You reach for the blindfold.

"Sorry," Vivalzi says. "That stays on for now."

"But when can I take it off?" you ask.

"When the Altair Group approves of you. If they do."

Her hand grips yours. She helps you out of the car and leads you towards an unseen destination. Your imagination races! Is their headquarters some kind of research lab, flush with the latest in forensic tools? Or maybe it's some sort of secret spy facility, with futuristic gadgets and technology?

Vivalzi stops. She knocks on a unseen door.

Tap! Tap-tap! Tap-tap-tap! Tap!

It's obviously a secret knock. You hear several locks turning, a rattle of chains, and then a creaky squeak as a door opens. With a firm grip, she leads you through it.

Even without sight, you sense many eyes are on you.

"Who is this, Doctor?" asks a deep, authorative voice.

"The police chief's son," Vivalzi replies, to a chorus of gasps. "Wait! He's a good investigator! He wants to help."

"No, no, no!" cries a scratchy, older man's voice. "He could be a spy! An infiltrator! It's too risky!"

Turn to page 24.

You shake your head. "I'm sorry, Dr. Vivalzi. I want to solve the crime but, well, this just *seems* a little crazy."

She stops the car—right in the middle of the street!

"Get out, then," she says in disgust. "Go back and help your dad scapegoat that chump Oswald. Meanwhile, while you guys are trying to cover things up, we real detectives will conduct a true investigation and find out who really killed John F. Kennedy!"

You get out of the car, stung by her rebuke. She drives away with a squeal of rubber.

Quickly getting your bearings, you realize you're only a few blocks away from Dealey Plaza. You start jogging that direction, but something stops you dead in your tracks. On a nearby telephone pole, you see a flyer with Kennedy's face on it. The headline screams "WANTED FOR TREASON"!

You tear it off and read it. It declares him guilty of seven "treasonous" activities, such as turning over control of the U.S. to the "communist-controlled United Nations." As you look up the street, you see dozens more flyers up on poles.

With a sad sigh, you start running towards Dealey Plaza again, pulling down flyers all along the way.

Turn to page 26.

"I'm not an infiltrator!" you retort. "I'm a detective! I may just be a kid, but I know a thing or two about crime solving. And I'll do anything I can to help solve this case!"

The room grows quiet, save for the sound of whispers. After a long pause, someone steps directly in front of you and removes your blindfold. Before you stands the deep-voiced man, his eyes dark and haunted. Behind him are Vivalzi and two others. All eyes are on you.

"Admission to the Altair Society requires a loyalty test," says the dark-eyed man. "Are you willing to take it?"

"Just tell me what I have to do," you say.

"It's simple, really," he says. "I want you to retrieve evidence from Dallas police headquarters."

"But evidence tampering is a felony!" you say in shock.

"You're absolutely right," he replies, "and it's happening at this very minute inside police headquarters. Any evidence that might point to conspiracy, or might exculpate Mr. Oswald, will be buried or destroyed unless we stop it. Unless you do!"

"But I don't even know you!" you counter.

"I was a spy in my former life," he says. "My code name was 'Joab.' I've seen dozens of government cover-ups. Heck, I led a few myself. But when I learned just how vicious the military-industrial complex had become, I resigned and formed the Altair Society to expose its crimes."

"Like what?" you start to answer. "Can't you just tell—"

"No! I'll tell you everything once you've proven your loyalty. Everyone else here has passed this test. If you want join us, you'll have to pass it, too."

What a dilemma! You want to help solve the crime, and the Altair Society sounds like they already have a good head start. But you never imagined that cracking the case would require you to break the law!

If you agree to steal evidence from police headquarters, turn to page 40.

If you refuse to break the law, turn to page 35.

You arrive at Dealey Plaza, where dozens of distraught people are scattered about. And right in the middle of it all, whom should you see but your rival Jenni Mudd herself! With her notepad and pencil in hand, she's interviewing witnesses like an old pro.

When she looks up and sees you, she scowls fiercely.

Oh, wait—that must've been a trick of the sunlight. She's actually smiling at you.

"Hey, what are you doing here, Turtleneck?" she asks.

"What do you think, Jenni?" you reply. "I'm here to solve the murder of the President!"

Turn to the next page.

"Me too. Why don't we work together?" she asks with a smirk. "I mean, I've already interviewed two dozen witnesses while *you* were off goofing around, but I don't mind letting you play catch-up. I'm used to that by now."

Always the smart-aleck. And she's not even done yet!

"Most of the eyeball wits—excuse me, that's investigator lingo for *witnesses,* if you didn't know—they say the shots came from over behind that fence. But in my professional opinion, they probably just heard the echo ..."

She trails off nonchalantly, daring you to ask her why.

Against your better judgment, you do. "Why, Jenni? Why do you think so many witnesses are wrong?"

"Because," she says smugly, "I *also* just interviewed a Dallas cop named Roger Craig who said they found a rifle up *there*." She points towards an open window on the sixth floor of the book depository.

"Oh, I know all about that already," you reply casually. "It was 7.65 Mauser. That's a German rifle. Bolt-action, if you didn't know."

"Yeah, that's what I heard, too," she says, trying to hide her disappointment. She kicks at a piece of dirt for a moment, then asks quietly, "So are we a team, Turtleneck?"

Same old Jenni—snide in victory *and* defeat. But even though she's obnoxious, she *is* pretty smart. Plus, she's got FBI contacts through her dad. She'd make a great partner.

"Yeah," you say, shaking her hand, "let's get started."

She shakes it with a fierce grip, then corrects you: "I already started."

Ugh! Always the wiseacre!

"So, I've got a few hot leads," she says. "I interviewed a man named Zapruder who may have caught the whole shooting on film. His film is at Kodak now, by Love Field, but I might be able to pull some strings and get us a screening."

Wow! That's sounds promising!

"Then again, we might want to check out the Depository while the crime scene is fresh," she continues, "Or, we could take our chances at Parkland Hospital—that's where they took the President's body. I know how you *love* examining entrance wounds, right, Detective?"

Sounds like she's *still* smarting over your crack work on the Billy shooting at the Packard place! But you shrug it off. You've got so many possible leads in the JFK shooting to explore! You wish you had a whole investigative team to explore all of them at once! But there's only two of you, and you'll have to pick one.

If you check out the book depository, turn to page 42.

If you go to Parkland Hospital, turn to page 47.

If you investigate the film evidence, turn to page 46.

Unable to help yourself, you rebuke Fannuci, "You can't coach a witness like that, Sergeant. It's criminal! The suspect doesn't even match her earlier description. He's not dark-haired, stocky or ruddy-faced! What if you've got the wrong guy?"

The room gets dead quiet. On the other side of the screen, the three clean-cut suspects scowl towards the screen. They obviously didn't like what they heard.

Lee Harvey Oswald, however, sneers, "I'm the only one in the t-shirt among these men. Naturally, I'll be picked out."

Fanucci puts an arm over you, still smiling strangely, "Come with me, kid." He leads you through the hall and into a nearby custodial closet. He closes the door.

"Now look, kid," Fanucci says, through a tight-lipped grin. "We found a pistol on this guy, bullets in his pockets, a fake ID. He's admitted to being a Castro-loving commie who lived in Mother Russia just a few years back. We found a rifle at his workplace—"

"I admit—it all sounds terrible," you reply. "But does that make it okay for you to coach witnesses or rig police lineups? Those are felonies. Don't you realize that none of this tainted evidence will be admissible at his trial?"

Fannuci's smile uncurls into a menacing scowl.

"Listen here, kid," he growls. "We got the FBI and CIA both saying Oswald's the guy who shot Kennedy—"

"How would *they* know? Our investigation just started!"

"No—the investigation is *over*. We're just gilding the lily. You can either help us or get out. But if you start rocking the boat, griping about rigged lineups, or witness tampering, and, well ..."

He doesn't have to finish. You know a threat, even when it's unspoken!

If you agree to let Oswald take the rap, turn to page 34.

If you tell Fanucci you won't go along with this, turn to page 57.

This whole line-up looks like a clear-cut case of witness tampering. But something tells you to stay quiet about it.

Oswald, however, can't help but protest.

"You know what you're doing—you're trying to railroad me," he says angrily. "You're doing me an injustice by putting me out here dressed different than these other men. This isn't fair!"

The men cuffed on either side of him begin dragging him towards the exit. They're obviously plainclothes cops!

"I know my rights. Why can't I speak to a lawyer?" he complains as he's led out of the basement.

The whole scene is too much for the witness. Helen Markham breaks into another round of hysterical crying. This time, it's Fanucci who comforts her.

"It's all right. You did good," Fanucci tells her gently. "You won't have to see him again. I promise."

Go on to the next page.

"Oh yes she will," you say, to no one in particular. "When she takes the witness stand in Oswald's trial."

Fanucci shoots you a strange look, then smiles. "Oh, right. Sure."

She again bursts into tears, and he escorts her out of the room. The rest of the cops clear out, too, leaving you alone with your thoughts.

But then it suddenly hits you. The murder of President Kennedy will be the highest-profile trial in American history. If the Dallas police are tampering with witnesses and denying Oswald his basic right to an attorney, they're running the risks of jail time and even a possible mistrial!

But maybe they don't plan to let this ever go to trial? the keen detective's voice in your head muses. *After all, Vivalzi said Oswald wasn't even guilty—he was being framed. Which would explain a lot.*

But if it's true that Oswald is just an innocent man being framed, he may be in danger of more than staged line-ups!

You rush upstairs to your dad's office.

Go on to the next page.

Your father is staring blankly into space when you rush into his office. His lips are moving silently.

"Dad!" you blurt out. "I have reason to believe Oswald's life may be in danger!"

Your father startles to life. "Who's Oswald?"

Argh!

"The *suspect!*" you reply. "Lee Harvey Oswald? The guy accused of killing President Kennedy?"

A voice from behind asks, "Why would you say that?"

You turn to see Fanucci, standing in the doorway, wearing that strange smile of his. You try to stay cool.

"Well, Sergeant," you say, "there's a lot of angry people out there, right? They want blood. What if one of them decides to kill Oswald right out in the halls?"

"You got a good point, kid," he replies. "I'll make sure we have extra cops around him while he's in the station. We'd *hate* for something to happen to him."

Then he puts an arm over your shoulder and gives you a painfully strong squeeze.

"Meanwhile," he says to your father, "Looks like we've got our man, Chief. We probably oughta let your son here head home? Take care of Mom and that lovely sister?"

Your father surfaces from his idiotic stupor long enough to agree, saying, "Oh. Yes. Right. Tell your mother we've, uh, you know... got our man."

It's really obvious now that Fanucci wants you out of the way. Now you're even more worried that Oswald's life might be in danger! But without your dad's blessing, you won't be welcome at the station. What should you do?

If you decide to take Fanucci's advice and quit the case, turn to page 34.

If you decide to bike home and ask your Mom's advice, turn to page 52.

If you wait for a ride from your Dad, turn to page 55.

Despite your misgivings about rigged line-ups and concerns about Oswald's safety, you decide to quit the case.

Two days later, Oswald is gunned down on live television. His killer is a Dallas nightclub owner named Jack Ruby. And while he's a stranger to the world, he isn't to you. You saw him Friday night, standing outside Oswald's interrogation room. He shook hands in a strange, ritualistic way with Sergeant Fanucci. And when Fanucci said, "You can take a shot at him," you realize now he wasn't just talking to you. *(Unless, of course, you chose to ask your father what Vivalzi means back on page 3 and totally missed that part. In which case, whoops! Continuity error!)*

But it's too late to do anything now. You had every opportunity to protest the witness tampering of the Dallas Police force. But you chose silence. And you had ample reason to fear the suspect's life was in danger. But rather than try to protect him, you chose to walk away.

There's a word for people who act like you've acted. People who choose the path of least resistance instead of taking a stand. People who shrink in the face of criminality, rather than confront it.

But this is a children's book parody—and we'd rather not include obscenities in it.

YOU LOSE

"I'm sorry, I want to help the Altair Society solve the crime, but I can't afford the price of admission," you tell them. "Not if I have to become a criminal to catch one."

Vivalzi lets out an angry groan, but the dark-eyed man rebukes her. "No, Vera, don't. Please."

Joab takes your hand and shakes it firmly. "I admire your integrity. You remind me of myself, a long time ago."

He looks away with a wistful sigh, still shaking your hand. Then suddenly, with lightning speed, his other hand flies up behind your ear. He pinches your neck. Suddenly, your legs buckle beneath you and you pass completely out!

You awaken hours later in a field of tall grass, a starry sky overhead. You can see the Dallas skyline on the horizon. The moon hangs over the city. It looks like it's frowning.

You start walking. It takes a couple of hours, but you finally get back to the city, and eventually to Dallas Police Headquarters. The place is still crowded with reporters and cops, but they've been joined by a small army of FBI agents. And they're acting like they run the place. They're barking orders at cops and carting off all the evidence the Dallas Police had collected during the day.

Two days later, Oswald is shot dead on live television. The FBI, now completely in control of the investigation, blames him and him alone for the assassination of Kennedy. You know it can't be true—not if the police reports of target practicing shooters in Dealey Plaza are to be believed.

But the reports have gone missing.

YOU LOSE

"I'm sorry, Director Hoover," you say. "It's an honor, but I think I'll just focus on fighting crime here in Dallas."

Hoover replies curtly, "Suit yourself." *Click*.

Your attentions turn back to the television, where an ambulance has just carried off the ashen and unconscious Oswald to Parkland Hospital, the same place where President Kennedy himself died only two days before.

"They're not going to save him," your mother whispers.

"How can you be so sure, Mom?" you reply weakly. "It was just a, a shot to the gut, right? Maybe the doctors—"

Her keen eyes train on you. "Don't play the fool with me, son. You know as well as I what this means. They're silencing the suspect. If your father couldn't protect him at the department, they certainly won't be able to at Parkland."

Less than an hour later, her prophecy comes to pass. Oswald is declared dead at Parkland. She turns off the TV and sits beside you. A strange focus lights her eyes.

Finally, she asks, "What business could you possibly have with Mr. J. Edgar Hoover? What haven't you told me?"

You can't bring yourself to lie to her. You tell her everything—Oswald's note, the FBI visits to his home, Ruby's secret handshake—and Fanucci's joke about "taking a shot." You even tell her about Hoover's ultimatum.

"What on earth could he blackmail you with, son?"

"Nothing, Mom!" you stammer. "It, it was just an empty threat to, to keep me from telling the press about his FBI screw-ups! He wanted me to just go along with his Oswald-acted-alone story, even though I ... I ... I knew I shouldn't!" You burst into guilty tears. "Oh, God, what have I done?!"

A grim smirk darkens her lovely face. "Well, then ... Congratulations, son. You've done your small part to help cover up an unspeakably evil crime." She starts to cry. But she's not finished. "Because you were too weak to speak truth to power. I hope it was worth it."

And in that awful moment, you forever lose the respect of the smartest, kindest mom in the world. And her love.

It wasn't worth it. Not even close.

YOU LOSE

"Criminal investigations are in my blood, Director!" you reply. "I'm happy to fill any opening you've got!"

"That's just what I like to hear!" he says. And with that, you've got a new, after-school job as a junior detective for the FBI! Your mom, despite her shock, beams with pride, and says, "My brilliant son ... I know you'll make history someday."

You settle in to your new digs at the Dallas FBI, but after a week of only being given incredibly mundane office duties, you're beginning to question your decision. You thought you'd be out investigating official FBI cases—but you're just stuck behind a desk answering phone calls for more important people. Like the janitor.

It's a sign of just how miserable your life has become that you're actually delighted one afternoon when your old kid detective rival, Jenni Mudd, pops her head in the door.

"Jenni, hey!" you exclaim. "It's so great to see you! But what are you doing here?"

"I should ask you the same thing," she says drily, hopping up on your desk. "I actually thought you had some integrity. Boy, was I wrong! How much did it take for you to sell out your JFK investigation? Thirty pieces of licorice?"

Your face flushes red with shame. You want to defend yourself, but you know she's right. So instead you ask, "So really, Jenni, why *are* you here?"

Without missing a beat, she replies, "Because even if *you're* off the JFK investigation, I'm not! And I'm about to crack the case wide open!"

Drat! If Jenni solves the case, she'll be the most famous detective in the world! And then she'll NEVER shut up!

"So," you ask, trying to sound nonchalant, "who do you think did it?"

"Why would *you* care?" she asks, "Didn't you promise Director Hoover you'd leave the JFK case alone?"

She's got a point. You and Hoover made a deal, and so far, you've lived up to it. But then again, you came to the FBI to solve crimes—not to be the Girl Friday for Lupé the Cleaning Guy!

After watching you twist in the wind for a spell, Jenni smiles coquettishly and says, "So—are you volunteering to come out of retirement to help me solve this case? Because if you are, I'll tell you everything I've learned so far about mind-controlled assassins. And you are not going to believe how crazy it sounds!"

If you agree to help, turn to page 60.

If you decline, turn to page 90.

"Taking evidence away from those who would destroy it isn't a crime in my book," you reply. "It's a duty."

"Spoken like a true member of the Altair Society," says Agent Joab, clapping you on the shoulder.

The three other members join him in giving you a hearty welcome. But the well-wishing has hardly begun when Joab turns to Vivalzi.

"Dr. Vivalzi," Joab says. "Did Dallas police file written reports about the target shooters at the Dealey Plaza fence?"

"Yes, of course."

"We need to get those reports before they disappear." he tells her. "The Feds want to pin this on Oswald alone, but if we can get those reports to the press—"

"Got it!" Vivalzi says, as she leads you out to the car.

You hop in the car. Vivalzi drives like a woman possessed back to Dallas Police Headquarters. It's even more crowded than it was earlier, a fact that clearly displeases her.

"All right," she says, "You're the chief's son. You should have no problem getting in to Evidence Control. When you do—"

"Wait. You're not going with me?" you ask nervously.

"I can't," she says. "Fanucci's a mobbed-up cop. And he's part of this somehow. I know it, and he knows I know it. If he sees me near the station, he'll know something's up."

She checks her watch, then says, "Hurry. Look for reports from November 20."

"Got it," you say, getting out of the car.

"If you find anything else important," she calls out, "any other evidence of foreknowledge, or conspiracy, or—"

"I know. I'll get it!" you reply over your shoulder as you jog up towards the entrance.

Once inside, you find yourself again in a bustle of TV news reporters, cameramen and cops. You weave in and out of crowds, heading towards the basement stairs. You're careful to avoid any live cameras as you skulk through the hall. Finally, you make it! With no one looking, you slip quietly down the stairs, heading for Evidence Control.

The room is a maze of evidence racks, organized by date. You weave your way quickly through the corridors, looking for the most recently collected evidence.

You see an aisle marked "Active Cases, 1963." That's it! You dart towards it, ready to grab the report and run.

But standing right in the middle of the aisle is Sergeant Fanucci! He's got a box in his hands, which he seems to be filling up, not unloading.

"Hey, kid!" he says, with an oversized grin. "What are you doing here? I thought you'd run off with Vivalzi."

"Nah," you reply coolly. "Turns out she's a kook."

"No kidding!" he laughs. "Well, glad you're back, though we've just about wrapped this one up. Got the rifle, casings. Found loads of Commie literature at Oswald's place. He's guilty as Judas. He made it too easy, if you ask me."

You've got to get rid of him if you're going to get that report. You'll have to distract him—but how?

If you tell him your dad asked you to retrieve this week's police reports, turn to page 63.

If you tell him you saw Vivalzi snooping around the station, turn to page 62.

The depository has been secured by police. But the cop guarding the entrance recognizes you and waves you through with a smile, saying, "Sixth floor, Detective."

You take the stairs. Coming out on the sixth floor, you realize it's one giant open space. Boxes are stacked everywhere, creating little walkways. It's a bit of a mess.

Several cops are congregated in the southeast corner. Boxes are stacked there, too, some right by the window.

A sheriff's deputy recognizes you and smiles. It's Roger Craig—the 1960 Dallas Police Officer of the Year! With a gentle drawl he says, "That there's the sniper's nest, son."

"May I?" you ask, gesturing to the windows.

"Yep—just be mindful you don't touch anything."

The leftmost window is cracked halfway. You slide into a shooter's position, careful not to disturb evidence. You ask Jenni for her camera. She reluctantly hands it to you.

You raise the lens to your eye and take a look down Elm Street. Jenni points down in front of Dealey Plaza, saying, "The witnesses all say the car was past that Stemmons sign when the last shot killed Kennedy."

"Zowie!" you exclaim. "He must've been a master marksman to pull that off! How many shots did he take?"

Jenni checks her notebook and says, "I've got witness reports of three, four, six, even eight shots."

You turn to the deputy and ask, "Find any cartridges?"

He nods and points over to your right, where you can see three shells scattered across the floor.

He says, "We found three. They were all side by side, an inch or two apart, and pointed in the same direction."

"So why aren't they still?" Jenni asks, half-shocked.

"Cap'n Fritz picked them up for a photographer," he replies, "then he just threw them down over there."

Jenni shakes her head in disgust, "Your dad's guys *really* know how to protect a crime scene! Picking up evidence and throwing it around? That's wonderful!"

You wish you could disagree, but she's right! But something is bothering you even more than that.

"So the shells were all next to each other," you ask, "but doesn't a bolt-action Mauser just spit out the casings?"

"Queer, ain't it?" he says sarcastically. "Guess the shooter musta picked 'em up after and put 'em that way."

You lean down towards the nearest casing, then pull out a pocket ruler you conveniently keep in your back pocket. You hold it over the spent shell, mindful not to touch it.

"This just isn't possible," you mutter to yourself, all but daring Jenni to ask you why.

She looks at the casings, trying to discern the problem. Finally, she relents and asks, "Why not?"

"These are 6.5 millimeter casings," you note. "So how'd Oswald get them into a 7.65 millimeter Mauser?"

She looks utterly baffled. You savor the payback.

"Deputy, are you *sure* the rifle you found was a Mauser?" you ask, "Could you have misidentified it?"

"Doubt it, son," he replies, "Seein' how four of us saw the words '7.65 Mauser' stamped right on the barrel."[176]

Jenni's jaw drops in shock, and you reply, "Let's go, Jenni, looks like we've got a gun to find."

"Come on," she replies, "My Vespa's right downstairs." How convenient!

Turn to the next page.

Minutes later, you and Jenni are racing westward by Vespa through the traffic of downtown Dallas. Pockets of grim-faced bystanders congregate all up Commerce Street—some still clutching small American flags, some weeping.

In a few minutes, you're back at the Municipal Building, racing through halls still clogged with reporters and cops, Jenni right on your heels. You weave nimbly through narrow openings between the men of law and print, patted on the back or hailed as "Detective" every so often by those policemen who know you as your father's secret brain trust.

Jenni takes note, impressed, as she tries to keep up. "Wow, Turtleneck—they actually like you for some reason."

You turn and shoot her an annoyed look as you keep racing forward—then see her eyes go suddenly wide at the sight of something ahead of you. But before you can turn back, you've collided head on with the object of her attention—the suspect himself!

His left eye is black from some recent wound—and he glares back at you, irritated at your carelessness.

"You should watch where you're going," he whispers.

"Sorry," you reply, flustered, "I'm, I just—"

Oswald's grim-faced police escort tugs him along, "Come on, let's go."

But Oswald stays for the moment—now looking directly at Jenni Mudd.

"You again?" he says with a strange, knowing smirk.

The color drains from her face—she's speechless!

Oswald's escort forces him ahead: "Move it." And the moment passes.

Your keen detective's mind floods with a million questions you should've asked Oswald. About the gun. The bullets. His motive. But your moment is past—yet there's one question you CAN ask. Of Jenni.

"What was THAT all about, Jenni?"

"I saw him," she says faintly, "last week. At the Santa Fe Building. I was visiting my dad. He came in looking for somebody. Then he left a note."

"What?!" you reply in shock. "**WHAT?!**"

Before you can say another word, Jenni steers you suddenly into a nearby janitorial closet.

"What are you telling me, Jenni?" you continue. "That the suspected assassin of the President of the United States of America was visiting the Dallas FBI a week ago? To meet with somebody?! *Is that what you're saying?!*"

Suddenly, to your absolute shock, she grabs you and kisses you hard on the lips! You feel yourself getting light-headed—heat rushing through every limb!

She breaks away for a moment. "You can't tell anybody that, Turtleneck. You can't. Promise me."

She leans slowly to kiss you again. Your keen teenage mind prepares to unleash a million rebukes. But your keen teenage body has only one thing to say: *ZOWIE!*

If you let your brain do the talking, turn to page 66.

If you let her hear your body talk, body talk, turn to page 70.

"Film evidence is a lot better than witness testimony," you say, parroting her know-it-all tone. "Witnesses make mistakes, or lie. But film evidence won't do either."

Jenni, not content to be lectured, ups the condescension ante even further, sniffing, "*Obviously.* But only someone with FBI connections will be able to get us to it. Hmmm, who might that be, Detective Turtleneck?"

"*You do, Jenni,*" you reply, defeated.

With a satisfied nod, she says, "That's right. *I* do." She checks her notes, "Now, this might take a little work on my end. So go home. I'll call you when I get a line on the film."

"But shouldn't I stay here and investigate the crime scene?"

"Sure," she says sarcastically, raising a phantom phone to her ear. "If you have some magic cableless phone in your pocket that I can reach you on out here, dummy!"

A cableless phone. How absurd!

"All right, I'll go home and wait for your call," you sigh.

And wait you do. Friday. Saturday. You sit by the phone in agony watching history unfold on TV, wishing you could interview the suspect or inspect the crime scene. Then, on Sunday at noon, you watch in absolute horror as Oswald is shot right on live TV! And yet, Jenni *still* hasn't called!

By Monday, you're certain she was just getting you off the case—when suddenly, the phone rings. It's her!

"Boy, Turtleneck, your dad sure cocked up the prisoner transfer, huh? Guess there won't even be a trial now!"

"What about the *film*? Was this just a fool's errand?"

"Maybe, since you're on it," she replies. "It's screening tonight. At KRLD studios. But I can't go. Can you?"

"And how!" you reply. "It's about time we see if this was worth the wait!"

Turn to page 50.

You hop on Jenni's conveniently placed Vespa and race to Parkland Hospital. The parking lot swarms with hurried police, grim Secret Service agents, and upset citizens. And there, right at the emergency room entrance, is the Presidential limousine. Your keen detective eyesight catches an intriguing sight. There's a bullet hole in the front window! Someone has also put the removable bubble top back on it, and to your horror, the whole car is being wiped clean! [175]

"That's a crime scene!" you cry out, to no one in particular. "You're ... you're destroying evidence!"

A Secret Service agent near you growls back as he wipes something jellylike off the trunk, "Shut up, Nancy."

Jenni rushes over and grabs your arm, whispering, "Come on, let's go inside."

Despite your misgivings, you relent and follow Jenni through the emergency room entrance.

Turn to the next page.

Inside the emergency room lobby, the scene is no less chaotic—doctors, nurses, cops and Secret Service agents in a pandemonium of grief and even hostility. You weave through the bedlam towards the nurses' station, hoping against hope for a chance to examine the President's wounds.

A doctor nearby cries out to the nurses, "Which room?"

A crying nurse points towards Trauma Room 1. The doctor races away. You're just about to follow him when, to your horror, a dark-suited man—no doubt an FBI agent—tries to follow him. Suddenly, a Secret Service agent with a Thompson submachine gun steps right in front of the agent and smashes the gun into his face! He drops like a rock, his jaw obviously broken.

Jenni takes hold of your sweater, whispering into your ear, "We can't go in."

"This is a state crime, Jenni!", you blurt out. "The Secret Service's job is to protect the President while he's alive! Not interfere with an investigation when they've completely screwed up! They have no jurisdiction over this!"

"They may not have jurisdiction, Turtleneck," she replies, "but they've got machine guns."

Drat! You hate to admit it, but she's right. If the Secret Service is willing to break the jaws of FBI agents, they'd surely do worse to you.

"Oh, *fiddlesticks!*" you reply, exasperated.

Jenni shares your disappointment, but shrugs. "We're probably better off searching for evidence elsewhere."

"Yeah, sure," you answer bitterly. "Most of it's either being washed away from the President's limo, or right there in the trauma room with the President himself! It's not like we're going to find anything useful out here in the hallway!"

In impotent rage, you kick a nearby stretcher. It careens into the wall. Suddenly, you hear a jangling sound, as a small object rolls off it and onto the floor at your feet.

Jenni does a double-take, her eyes bulging comically. "Is that what I think it is?"

You lean over the object, then pick it up with a pair of tweezers you conveniently had in your pocket. It's a bullet, in nearly pristine condition!

You take out your handy magnifying glass, then examine the bullet carefully.

"It's a bullet, all right," you answer, amazed. "Looks like it's been fired—but it hardly seems like it hit anything."

Suspicious, muses your inner detective voice, *like it was planted here to be found ...*175

Jenni examines the bullet herself, sighing, "I hate to say it, Turtleneck, but you're right. We should turn this over to the FBI—my dad could get it to the ballistics lab. They might be able to learn something about it. And I bet he'd let us stay on the investigation, since we found it!"

Turn it over to the feds? You're not really sure it wouldn't be better off going back to the evidence room at police headquarters, especially given all the evidence destruction you've already witnessed!

If you turn the bullet over to the FBI, turn to page 74.

If you decide to take the bullet back to the Dallas Police instead, turn to page 78.

You arrive at KRLD studios Sunday night. Reporters are rushing in and out of every door. Cars careen in and out of the parking lot. You slip quietly in through the back door.

Once inside the studio, you see three grim men in suits, strolling purposefully down a hallway. You notice a gold star on the lapel of one of the men's suits. Secret Service! You follow them, as inconspicuously as possible.

The men enter a small, dark room at the end of the hall. You step in, taking out your notebook and pencil. No one pays you any mind—all eyes stare at the projector screen on the opposite wall. You stand in the darkness by the projector. Right beside you is a dark-haired man in his early thirties, dressed in a sweat-stained suit. He's holding a notebook and pencil. You turn to him nervously.

"Is this ... is this where they're screening the uh, film of, uh, the assassination?" you ask him.

"It sure is," he responds, in a gentle Texas accent. "And I'm as curious as a cat in a kosher deli on Christmas Eve."

What the?! That doesn't even make sense! Then it hits you: this isn't just another reporter, it's CBS Southern Bureau chief Dan Rather! He's a rising star of journalism, and you've seen his reporting on this nonstop since Friday!

You're about to congratulate him on his excellent work, but before you can, the lights go out, and the projector starts to whirr. The Secret Service agents fold their arms and stare grimly at the screen.

The film is grainy, but you can make out President and Mrs. Kennedy, riding in the back of the open limo. Suddenly, his head seems to explode, and it jolts violently toward the back and left. Dan Rather gasps. One of the Secret Service men shakes his head slowly. You watch as Mrs. Kennedy climbs onto the back of the car—what could she be doing?

The sight is so horrifying, it takes you a minute to realize it—the shots came from the front, not the back! How could Oswald have killed him if he was shooting from a building *behind* the limousine? *There were other shooters!*

The film shudders to an end, and the room goes silent.

Go on to the next page.

The Secret Service men slowly file out, followed by the projectionist, who looks like he's about to throw up. You turn to Dan Rather. "Did ... did you *see* that?! The shots that killed him came from the *front*, not behind!"

Rather nods in agreement. "They sure did, son," he says sadly. "They took his top off faster than Katie Lynn's blue silk necktie in June, and now I'm as confused as a rabbit trying to shoot pool on a frozen lake in January. But facts are facts. And I've gotta report 'em as I see 'em." *174*

He slowly walks out of the room, leaving you to try to interpret his inscrutable similes. You notice that the projectionist, in his rush to get to the bathroom, left the film in the machine. Maybe you should take it, you think! After all, the Dallas police have juristiction over the case, and you're working for them! On the other hand, Dan Rather saw what happened—surely he'll tell the American people the truth about what took place! As you try to make up your mind, you hear footsteps in the hallway, slowly approaching the room.

_____

If you take the film to reveal it to the public, turn to page 79.

If you trust Dan Rather to report it like he sees it, turn to page 80.

52

You exit the police station to see the purple haze of dusk. You hop on your bike and pedal the dark miles home.

Your mother greets you at the door with teary eyes and a long, loving hug. She's waited up for you, and has a warm dinner and hot chocolate set out.

"Son, what did you learn today?" she asks quickly. "Your father's been incoherent, as usual. The TV reports are peculiar, to say the least. But I know you must know more by now. What really happened, son?"

"Mom, you won't believe what's going on up there!" you reply. You then recount the day's events in crisp detail: the FBI note, the rigged line-up, along with every other suspicious detail you can recall. She listens intently, piecing it together as you go. When you've finished, she surprises you with some facts of her own.

"I think you're on to something, son," she says. "I spoke with Jenni Mudd's mom, Linda, earlier today. She said Jenni spent the day in Dealey Plaza—"

"Oh man! Jenni's on the case, too?" you cry, annoyed.

"Yes," she says, "She interviewed dozens of witnesses at the crime scene. Linda said she's even planning to write a book about it! Most witnesses said they heard shots come from behind the Plaza fence. Some even saw gun smoke."

"Unbelievable!" you blurt out, "But if there were shooters behind the fence, why are they pinning it all on Oswald?"

"Tonight on TV, he said he was just a patsy. But if that's true, then he really *is* in danger, son," your mother says, squeezing your hand. "Tomorrow morning, I want you to go back up there and keep investigating this."

"But Sergeant Fanucci said I was off the case!" you say.

"I'll get you back on it, don't you worry," she replies.

You look at her skeptically. "But how, Mom?"

"You forget. I sleep with the Chief of Police."

"Oh, Mom! *Eewwwwwwwwwwwww.*"

She laughs heartily for the first time today. After the day you've had, you can't imagine a lovelier sound.

Go on to the next page.

Exhausted by the events of the day, you collapse on your bed, eager for a reprieve from all your stresses. Yet sleep proves no escape at all, as your dreams that night are haunted by visions of murder and intrigue.

You're riding in the Presidential limousine, waving to throngs of enthusiastic fans on a sunny Dallas day. Your lovely wife, Jenni Mudd (!), sits beside you in the car, wearing a pink Chanel suit and matching pillbox hat—and she's holding a bouquet of black roses.

As the limo turns from Houston onto Elm, it passes in front of the School Book Depository. You see Oswald standing in the doorway, watching you pass. His expression, unlike everyone else in the crowd, is one of pure terror. He's calling out to you, but you can't hear him over the din of the crowd.

As you drive slowly towards the grassy knoll, you see a black silhouette behind the fence. He's wearing a Jughead paper crown. It's your archenemy, Slugs O'Toole! He's pointing his pellet gun at *you!* Suddenly, everyone in the crowd pulls out rifles and handguns and begins firing at you in unison!

Turn to page 54.

54

You awake the next morning soaked in a cold sweat. Wait a minute—that's not sweat! Oh, no! You wet the bed for the first time in years! It's almost as if your subconscious mind is warning you to drop the case—*or else.*

Just as you begin to collect your thoughts, your mother enters your room with the good news.

"You're back on the case, son!" she beams. "Your father had a change of heart and decided perhaps there's more to this crime than meets the eye!"

With a kiss on your cheek, she leaves you to your thoughts. And your pee-stained sheets.

If you head straight to the police station, turn to page 84.

If you decide to change your pee-stained sheets first, turn to page 85.

You're so exhausted from the day's events that you decide to wait for a ride home from Dad. Fanucci, satisfied, leaves the office with a friendly wave.

"Thanks for the help, kid," he says as he exits.

But the chaos of the day isn't done, and despite your father's best attempts to extricate himself from work by dinner time, the steady stream of demands for his attention by others keeps him occupied late into the night.

Eventually, you grow tired of waiting around and wander out into the halls of the station. Though it's after midnight now, the place is still abuzz with activity and packed with cops and media. In fact, there seems to be a commotion coming from a large room nearby. *Hmmm...*

You enter the room from the back, to a flood of lights and reporters. At the head of the room, District Attorney Henry Wade is presiding over a press conference.

"Was he a member of any Communist front organizations?" asks a reporter in the crowd.

Wade drawls, "That I can't say at the present time..."

The reporter continues, "Any organizations that he belongs to that you know of?"

"Well, uh," he begins, "the only one I mentioned was the, uh, Free Cuba Movement or whatever that—"

A man beside you in the room calls out a correction: "The Fair Play for Cuba movement!"

Wait a minute, it's the balding fellow you saw in the halls earlier, talking to Fanucci. *He's a reporter?*

Turn to page 56.

56

You feel a hand on your shoulder and turn to see your father, looking at you sheepishly.

"Hey," he whispers, "I think the coast is clear. Let's get outta here before I get stuck here with even *more* work."

Yeesh, what a heel! The biggest case he'll ever possibly have and all he wants to do is run away from it!

You pop your bike in the trunk and hop in the car. You're off the case, but still as fascinated by the curiosities you'd just begun to uncover as your father is bored of them.

"So Dad," you say, as he begins driving out of the garage towards home, "What else did you uncover today? You must've learned a million amazing new things, right?"

"You're right, son," he replies, nodding, "I discovered rock solid proof of something amazing today, all right."

"What, Dad? Tell me!" you plead, your keen detective's mind consumed with curiosity.

"I found rock solid proof," he replies with an exhausted sigh, "That I *hate* having to work late! Why couldn't JFK have died somewhere else, you know? Miami or something?"

You couldn't be more ashamed.

You spend the rest of the weekend glued to the television, off the case but still obsessed with it. Until Sunday afternoon—when you watch in absolute horror as a man with a snubnosed .38 shoots Oswald in the gut on live TV!

Reporters soon reveal his identity. Jack Ruby. Dallas night club operator who called half the police force friends and clients. But you know him as someone else. The balding man impersonating a reporter at the midnight press conference. A guy who knew more about Lee Harvey Oswald than anyone else in the room. [174]

"How would a nightclub operator friendly with the Dallas police know so much about a Marxist loner who loved Cuba?" the keen detective's voice in your head muses.

But it doesn't matter now. You're off the case. It'll be up to better detectives to make sense of it in the days ahead. But they don't.

YOU LOSE

Though you can't help but be intimidated by his brute menace, you summon all your courage to stand up to him.

"Now you listen to me for a minute, Sergeant Fanucci," you say, as boldly as you can. "I don't know what America *you* live in, but *my* America stands for a few things. Equal justice under the law. The presumption of innocence until proven guilty. The right of due process."

He stares at you, stunned by your courage. He takes a step back, his hands reaching behind him. You feel patriotic fervor flowing through you like electricity!

"Now maybe this Oswald is a Marxist. Maybe he's even an assassin sent by Castro himself! But we're not in Russia, or Cuba, or even Sicily. This is America! And since you seem completely hellbent on ignoring the rule of law, you leave me no choice but to report you to Attorney General Robert Kennedy himself!"

But Sergeant Fanucci has heard enough. With blinding speed, he produces a small bottle and a heavy rag from his back pockets. He pours liquid from the bottle onto the rag—all of it—and steps towards you!

"Wait! Don't! You can't do this—*arghgh*!"

With his massive hands, he forces the rag over your nose and mouth. The ether fumes overwhelm you in seconds. Blackness overtakes you.

You slowly awaken, your head aching miserably. You try to open your eyes, but see only darkness. Something is covering them. You hear what sounds like the roar of a motor, and feel the steady *thump-thump-thump* of a boat cutting through waves, the occasional splash of mist upon your face. You try to reach up to remove whatever covers your eyes, only to find that your hands are cuffed behind your back. Then you try to kick—but your feet are utterly unmovable, as if they were encased in stone.

Or concrete, the detective within whispers quietly.

The first true pangs of panic strike you! You shake violently, trying to free your hands, but you simply don't have the strength!

Turn to page 58.

"A mafia execution by a Dallas cop," observes your inner detective coolly. "So the mob's tied into this somehow. But how?"

It'd be a fascinating thing to contemplate—if you weren't the one about to be executed.

Moments later, the engine stops. You can sense the boat slowing to a crawl. After a few seconds, you feel only a gentle rocking on small waves. The distant call of an osprey.

It's all so peaceful. For a moment, anyway.

"Sergeant Fanucci, if you're there—I'm begging you—"

Powerful hands reach under your armpits from behind you, lifting you with a throaty grunt. You thrash violently, hoping against hope to break free. But your desperation prompts only a vicious chuckle. You feel yourself being thrown forward—then violently pulled downward with a splash into the unseen waters.

Downward you sink, ever so quickly, into the bitterly cold blackness. Your blindfold comes off. The suddenness of your descent causes your ear drums to explode from the increased water pressure—the pain is beyond excruciating! You scream as the air is violently squeezed from your lungs—never to return. Your last coherent thought before raw, animal terror completely overwhelms you is of…

No, there is no other thought.

YOU LOSE

"I'll help," you tell Jenni. "Just tell me what you know."

Her face gets deadly serious. She closes the door to your office and asks you in a low whisper, "Are you familiar with the CIA's MK-ULTRA program?"

You shake your head. "Never heard of it."

"Color me surprised," she says with a smirk. "MK-ULTRA is a top secret CIA mind control program. They've conducted all kinds of illegal brainwashing experiments—even on innocent American civilians. They're using hypnosis and drugs to erase people's memories, or implant false ones. Even turning ordinary people into unwitting assassins!"

It all sounds like something from a James Bond story!

"What are you saying?" you ask. "That Oswald was some sort of mind-controlled hitman? But why? Why would the CIA want to kill President Kennedy? It makes no sense!"

Jenni feigns shock at your ignorance. "Cuba? 1961? Castro? *Hello?*"

She savors the clueless look on your face for a few moments before finally answering.

Go on to the next page.

"Kennedy fired CIA Director Allen Dulles because the CIA screwed up the Bay of Pigs invasion. Castro's forces crushed the CIA-backed Cuban exiles in three days—when Dulles told JFK the whole thing would be a cakewalk! Afterwards, Kennedy said he'd splinter the CIA into a thousand pieces. So they splintered *him* into pieces first!"

As horrifying as it sounds, it all makes sense. Especially considering that Allen Dulles was just named to LBJ's new Warren Commission to "investigate" the assassination. What better place would there be to orchestrate a CIA cover-up than on the official government investigative team?

"The CIA picked Oswald to brainwash because he was a Castro lover, right?" you blurt out as you connect the dots in your head. "So when he killed Kennedy, all of America would hate Castro even more!"

But then it hits you. None of this explains why Oswald was interacting with FBI Agent Hosty before the assassination.

Jenni reads your mind, saying, "So why was he talking to the FBI? That's the crazy part. He wasn't a Castro lover at all. He was a deep-cover agent. Behind all his Marxist talk, he was working for American intelligence. Spying on Marxist and pro-Castro groups inside the U.S. by pretending to be one. And informing the FBI on what he found!"

It seems crazy, but there's a certain spooky logic to it.

"Of course!" you exclaim as you jump from your chair. "*That's* why Hoover shut me down! If America found out Kennedy was killed by an undercover FBI informant, Hoover would've been strung up from a lightpost!"

But one thing still doesn't make sense to you. "So if Oswald was working with the FBI, why would the CIA brainwash him into being an assassin?"

"That's what *I* want to know," Jenni purrs, her eyes narrowing, "But I've found out about a CIA hospital that may be being used to create hypno-assassins. And I'm flying out there. Tonight. Want to come?"

If you agree to help her, turn to page 86.

If you choose to decline the offer, turn to page 90.

"Nice work, Sergeant," you say. "I wish I'd listened to you earlier. Instead, I got an earful of crazy conspiracy talk from Dr. Vivalzi. She even thinks the Mob is tied into this."

Fanucci's smile draws tight. "She does, huh?"

"Crazy, right?" you reply. "She even came back to the station. I just saw her snooping around upstairs a minute ago, looking for who knows what."

Fanucci lets out an uneasy chuckle, then puts the box down on the concrete floor.

"Tell ya what, kid," he says warmly. "Keep an eye on this for me. I'm gonna check on her. Sounds like she mighta gone off the deep-end, ya know? She may need help."

Without waiting for your reply, he springs past you. Your bluff worked like a charm!

You quickly dig through the box he placed on the floor. Part of you wants to take it all—but you'd look mighty suspicious lugging a boxful of evidence through a crowd of cops! You rifle through folders full of photos, fingerprints, witness reports, evidence from Oswald's home. Finally, you find a thick stack of police reports. There's dozens of them!

Wait—was that a door opening? Are those footsteps?

You quickly tuck the entire folder down the front of your pants and cover it with your shirt. Your heart races! An older police officer with a scar on his cheek rounds the corner.

"Sergeant Fanucci sent me," he says in an unfriendly tone. "Said I should relieve you of guard duty, detective."

"That was nice of him," you reply. "I'll be going then."

You head casually past him and back upstairs, the folders under your shirt. You work your way through the masses. It feels like every eye in the hall is watching you!

But finally, you make it back to the parking lot. You did it! You head quickly to Vivalzi's car and open the passenger door, saying, "That was almost too easy!"

But the driver's seat is empty. She's gone. You touch her seat. It's still warm. Leaning closely to it, you see fingernail marks scratched into the leather. Now you begin to smell the pungent odor of ether lingering in the air. Your clever bluff worked too well. It got Vivalzi kidnapped. And probably killed. Nice going, Sherlock.

YOU LOSE

"Yeah," you say, "Oswald made this case so easy, even my dad probably could've solved it."

Fanucci guffaws. "Ha! You said it, kid, not me!"

"Oh, that reminds me," you say casually. "My dad asked me to bring him this week's police reports. Said he wanted to make sure he'd signed off on everything before the feds take them."

He shrugs. "OK, sure. Might as well make sure we've crossed our t's and dotted our i's, right?"

He hands you a thick folder and says, "Just make sure you bring 'em back. Wouldn't want 'em to go missing, huh?"

"Exactly," you reply.

You take the reports with you. Once upstairs, you slip them under your turtleneck and into your pants, then weave your way back through the long hallway. Finally you're back outside. You jog to Vivalzi's car and slip into the passenger seat.

"Well?" she asks anxiously.

"Have I got a surprise for you," you say, as you reach into your pants. You pull out the folder and hand it to her.

She flips quickly through the stack, then lets out a big, triumphant laugh as she pulls out a report.

"You did it!" she says.

"Now can I join the Altair Society? Do you trust me?"

She smiles and nods her head. "You're one of us now. Now you're ready to join the real investigation."

She drives quickly and recklessly back to the hideout. And this time, you get to enjoy the trip without a blindfold.

Turn to page 64.

When you return to the Altair Society's secret hideout, you're greeted as a hero!

"You did it, son!" Agent Joab exclaims happily. He rifles through the reports and finds one dated November 20th, 1963, by a Captain George Doughty. He reads it aloud:

"Officers reported seeing two unknown men sighting in a rifle over fence in Dealey Park. Rifle being sighted in at two silhouettes in old model car in vicinity. Officers circled to contact men, but they disappeared."

Joab is delighted, adding, "These reports are *proof* of both foreknowledge *and* conspiracy. Multiple target shooters on the motorcade route a few days before the assassination? We could call a press conference right now and—"

But before he can finish his sentence, both the wild-eyed older man and his dark-haired peer burst into protests.

"No no no!" the old man hectors. "The *real* proof of conspiracy is 1,345 miles west of here, in Area 51! Kennedy was going to reveal our contact with alien life—"

"Come on, Professor Coppens!" the dark-haired man counters. "This has the Mafia's grubby fingerprints all over it, as payback for Kennedy's war on organized crime!"

"That's pure poppycock, Angelo!" Professor Coppens retorts. "You're letting your Italian heritage blind you!"

The two begin talking over each other, like a couple of bratty kids. Finally, Joab booms over all of them, *"Enough!"*

The group quiets quickly down, and Joab continues in a calmer voice, "You both have theories—promising ones. But my own gut tells me this is the handywork of the CIA. Kennedy had many enemies—the Mafia, Castro, the Russians. But the CIA, under Allen Dulles, has mastered the art of government overthrows, political assassinations, and cover-ups. They did it in Iran, The Congo, heck, they helped kill the Diem brothers in South Vietnam three weeks ago. After the CIA bungled the Bay of Pigs, Kennedy fired Dulles and promised to shatter his beloved CIA into a thousand pieces. But I think they beat him to the punch."

Go on to the next page.

Joab turns to you with a respectful nod. "Son, as our newest member, the honor falls to you to choose which path we'll investigate first."

Wow! The myriad of possibile suspects boggles even *your* keen detective's mind! You feel like Hercule Poirot in *Murder on the Orient Express*—where a dozen suspects all might've participated in the killing!

"If I'm going to mount an effective investigation," you reply, "I'll need more information. It sounds like lots of people had motives—but I can't tell who had the means and opportunity to pull this off!"

Joab nods. "Fair enough. Which of our theories do you want to know more about?"

If you ask Professor Coppens about his Area 51 theory, turn to page 94.

If you ask Angelo about his Mafia theory, turn to page 98.

If you ask Agent Joab about his CIA theory, turn to page 96.

"Jenni!" you reply in disbelief, "We've got an assassin who pays courtesy visits to the FBI a week before he pulls off impossible shots using bullets that don't fit his rifle who *then* takes the time to line up his shell casings neatly in a row on a windowsill when he should be running like heck! *Do you realize what this means?!*"

She looks at you pleadingly, her eyes growing moist, then whispers sadly, "Yes, I do. It means the end of the FBI. Robert Kennedy will shut it down. He hates Hoover, and if America finds out about this, they will, too. And my dad will be out of a job. And I'll never get to work there. That's my dream, you know?" Then she leans closer and says, "I *know* you know—we're both detectives, right? It's in our blood."

Before you can rebuke her for her self-centeredness, she kisses you again, more tenderly this time. But you push her back this time—you're not going to let her dissuade you!

"Jenni," you say sternly, "We're on to something *big* here—and there's more at stake for America than protecting our own self-interest. This is what police work *means*, Jenni—exposing the truth, all of it, however ugly it might be! *Fiat justitia ruat caelum, Jenni—let justice be done though the heavens may fall!*"

Huge tears are now rolling down her face—and you see, for the first time, that beneath all her bluster and sarcasm, she's still just a little girl. Scared and vulnerable.

Go on to the next page.

You place a brotherly hand on her shoulder and say, "I won't blame you for quitting the case, Jenni. It must be a shock—to find out this Oswald guy is the suspect, and he was talking to the FBI beforehand. But I hope you understand that I can't quit. I can't go home and pretend I don't know what I know—because what I *know* is that this is looking more and more like a frame-up job, and a sloppy one, too. Sloppier than Slugs O'Toole's frame-up of Bennie Geisler in *The Case of the Guilty Dog That Barked First*."

She laughs through tears in spite of herself, chuckling, "I'll never forget that one, Turtleneck—when you beat me on that case, I thought, 'I'll marry that dork one day.'"

You feel yourself blushing, then reach in to hug her. "One step at a time, Jenni."

Hugging you back, she replies, "Yeah. One step at a time." Then she pinches your shoulder in a strange place. And then you pass out.

Turn to page 68.

68

You emerge from the darkness in a haze—are those glowing flying saucers overhead? No, just bright lights—in a circle just above you. And above them, a clean, white ceiling.

"Where am I?" you mumble.

A friendly, paternal voice from behind you chuckles, then replies, "Welcome to beautiful Springfield, Missouri."

"But—I can't—feel my legs?"

The voice answers crisply, "Oh, don't worry—that's just the anaesthetic. Oh, and the restraints. But don't fret, you'll have your arms and your legs back in no time."

Wait—you're in a hospital. On an operating table. But what are they operating on? And how did you get here? You were just hugging Jenni a second ago—and now—?

For a moment, the doctor leans in front of your face. His breath smells like mint; his smile is bright. "I understand you *thought* you learned something that you couldn't have learned. But you're having trouble forgetting it?"

"No, no—" you reply weakly, "I learned ... the suspected assassin ... was meeting with FBI people last week ... and—"

He laughs warmly. "Oh, don't let that pesky little memory trouble you. We're going to take it right out. You'll be all better in no time."

Then his face vanishes, and you hear him whisper, "Nurse, can you hand me the striker, please?"

"Yes, Doctor."

A few seconds later, you hear a high, whirring sound. Then, suddenly, you feel vibrations through your skull—your teeth. They're cutting open your head! It's brain surgery!

But you're unable to move at all—immobilized from the neck down! You try to scream, but find only a whimper coming out. Then, you feel a dull heat boring into you from above. It's spreading slowly outward—like hot butter melting holes slowly through your brain.

Going slowly deeper in. Thoughts flash warmly across your mind—then vanish forever. Jenni. Kennedy. Craig. Mauser. Oswald. Dealey. Dad. Mom.

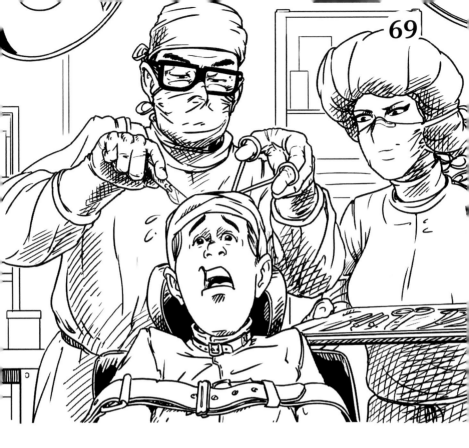

Help. Help. Help.

SNIP. SNIP. SNIP.

Then pain stop.

No more.

Feel fine.

Okay.

All better.

All better.

YOU LOSE

You hungrily surrender to Jenni's kiss—intoxicated by the absurd trangression of it all. Here you are, in a janitorial supply closet at Dallas Police Headquarters, locked in the passionate embrace of a girl you'd long regarded as an annoying, and occasionally superior, investigative rival. Only minutes ago, you'd learned of sniper's bullets that don't match their rifle. Of the conspicuous arrangement of spent shell casings on the windowsill of the depository by an assassin who surely should've been hastening his escape. Of FBI contact with a suspected assassin only days before the murder of the President of the United States.

You're on to something big, your conscience whispers.

Yet now, you're learning about the power of forbidden love—and you can't get enough of that funky, funky stuff!

After a small eternity of passionate kissing, Jenni pulls away from you—fixing you with her fiery, clever eyes.

"So—are you my boyfriend now, Turtleneck?"

You smile, half-amazed by the sound of your voice saying, "And *how!*"

She smiles back, brushing your mussed hair back into its perfect feather. "Then I want you to do something for me."

In your dizzying daydream rush of teenage hormones, you'd be willing to shoot LBJ himself if she'd asked it now! Yet she has only a modest request.

"If we drop the case—just this one case—I can get us both jobs with the FBI as soon as we graduate, working bigger cases than you've ever dreamed of. We could make history together, Turtleneck—the smartest crime-fighting couple in the history of the Bureau. Will you? For me?"

Her green eyes glisten like moist emeralds. She brings her thin, pale hands to cradle your face, looking back at you with an earnestness and affection you never would've believed her capable of. Her power over you is complete—and you nod back, no longer capable of choosing your own adventure. It's been chosen for you. You're off *The Case of the Assassinated President*—and now on *The Case of the Super-Whipped Sellout*.

Jenni leads you out of the closet, out of the station, off the case and into a future she'd formerly planned to live alone—that of a professional federal investigator.

In the years that follow, the love between you deepens and blossoms, and though you'd never have imagined it possible, you learn as much from her as she does from you. About the necessity of pragmatism. About compromise. About the futility of slavish idealism in the real world.

You both graduate at the top of your high school class—the first joint valedictorians in your school's history, and, after acing college, you're both welcomed into J. Edgar Hoover's massive intelligence bureau with lusty and delighted arms.

And Jenni's prophecy proves eerily correct—as a young, married couple in the FBI, you solve countless crimes together, against drug traffickers, domestic terrorists, and other menaces that make your old rival, Slugs O'Toole, look as pure as the driven snow!

Yet there are moments you find yourself conflicted with an assignment, or troubled by a request from FBI superiors. Requests not unlike the very one that Jenni made of you all those years ago, in the heat of young passion. To drop a case. Ignore a great lead. Look away from a troubling bit of evidence. Or bury it completely for the good of the country.

"Don't worry, Turtleneck," Jenni always replies in such moments with a sigh of feigned weariness. "I still love you, you damn softie."

Her sweet assurances always seem enough to ease your conscience, and refocus your mind on the greater good you've achieved. For you've both done so much of it—saving lives and imprisoning evildoers. And there's no ignoring her lesson—everyone has to make little sacrifices here and there. After all, what parent hasn't told a white lie to make a child feel better about an ugly piece of art? What spouse hasn't complimented an unflattering dress or silly tie when their beloved seeks approval? There are a lot of times when honesty must yield to diplomacy, and principle to pragmatism. For the sake of peace and happiness.

And Monday morning, April 25, 1977, proves one of them, when FBI Director Kelley invites you both into his office with a new assignment.

Turn to the next page.

"Well, you two lovebirds," he says, "we'd like your help on a JFK clean-up job. You're the go-to guys for that, right?"

Jenni replies, "Just tell us what we're looking for, sir."

"An unfortunate bit of film needs securing," he replies. "The House Select Committee on Assassinations just turned up something that, well, let's say it might open old wounds."

You nod dutifully, ready to go to work. "We're on it."

Within the week, thanks to called-in favors and a little cat burglaring, you've got your hands on the explosive piece of 8mm film. The HSCA never knew what hit them.

Jenni, with a mischevious look in her eye, asks you the obvious question. "Well, shall we? Before we turn it over?"

You're too curious to resist. In minutes, you're in an FBI conference room, loading a projector. Jenni kills the lights, and you sit together, watching the film on the screen.

The camera was in the back of a Jeep, riding roughly through a mossy, dark bayou of some sort—the backs of two men in military caps in the front seat. It's passing a sign with the shape of Louisiana on it.

"Lake Pontchartrain," Jenni says, "I've been there."

The film continues. Now the Jeep has stopped—and the camera takes in five men standing before it. Some look Cuban. A man in civilian garb—dark-eyed, haggard, and with a prominent nose turns quickly away from the camera.

"That looks like David Atlee Phillips," she says, "CIA Chief of Operations for the West." She's right—it does.

The camera turns to another group of men, standing by a truck. Cubans and whites in military gear—likely at one of the forbidden anti-Castro training camps in the early '60's.

"Phillips at an anti-Castro camp?" you shrug. "Seems pretty innocuous to me, really."

And then the camera trains on one man in particular, with a smirk you'd recognize anywhere. Lee Harvey Oswald. On film. At an anti-Castro camp. With what appears to be one of the highest-ranking CIA figures of the last 30 years.

If this film were to get out, it would rock the nation to its very core, proving beyond doubt Oswald's loyalties were not to Castro, or Russia. He was a CIA asset all along.

But thanks to you and Jenni, it never does.[173]

YOU LOSE

Against your natural instincts, you defer to Jenni's suggestion and hand her the evidence bag with the pristine stretcher bullet. She rushes to a pay phone in the nearby lobby and makes a call, breaking the news of your serendipitous discovery of evidence to her father.

"Dad," she says excitedly, "you won't believe what Turtleneck and I found over at Parkland just now. A bullet! Yeah—it may be tied to the shooting. And I've got two dozen witness interviews to turn over from Dealey. I'll tell you all about it when I get home. Love you, Dad!"

She hangs up, then rushes over to you, beaming.

"Great news, Turtleneck!" she says, "He said we can be on the research team when the official investigation begins!"

You gasp. "When the *official* investigation begins?"

"I didn't want to say anything before, but the FBI's taken over already. Any evidence the Dallas police find is going to Washington," she says, waving the bag, "including this. Dad said we should drop the case for now, and he'll call us when he's ready for our help."

What can you do but wait for the call?

Go on to the next page.

Jenni was right. The feds take over the investigation, impounding all evidence, including your bullet. But a few months later, Jenni calls you with happier news. You've both been asked to fly to Washington, DC, by a researcher for the Warren Commission named Arlen Specter.

On the flight out to DC, she fills you in.

"So, this Specter guy," she tells you, "He thinks our bullet may have been the one that killed the President and injured Governor Connally ..."

"That seems impossible," you reply skeptically. "The bullet was in pristine condition—hardly a scratch on it."

Jenni looks around the plane at other passengers, then lowers her voice to a whisper. "I know. The thing is, this Arlen Specter? He's a Freemason ... and so are LBJ, J. Edgar Hoover, Allen Dulles, and a lot of other guys who are on this Commission. Including my dad."

Freemasons? You've heard of them before, but always thought they were just harmless old men who liked to meet in private so they could wear silly aprons!

"What are you saying, Jenni?" you ask. "That the Freemasons had something to do with Kennedy's death?"

Jenni shrugs it off, then looks out the window of the plane at an endless expanse of moonlit clouds below, finally replying, "No, I don't know. But it's weird, don't you think? Freemasons are involved in all kinds of cult rituals. And they hate Catholics! I've even read that they practice secret kinds of magic—and that the killing of Kennedy might have been a part of their 'Killing of the King' ritual!"

Magic? Rituals? You laugh it off—it frankly sounds like Jenni might've gone off the deep end this time! That, or she's deliberately trying to mislead you.

You decide it probably doesn't matter. You're back on the case, right? And tomorrow morning, you'll be meeting with Arlen Specter and have a chance to help steer this investigation to completion!

Turn to page 76.

The next morning, you and Jenni arrive bright and early at Arlen Specter's office in DC. You knock on the door.

"Come in!" calls a friendly voice.

Specter greets you both with a warm smile. He's holding a Carcano rifle—Oswald's rifle! Beside his desk is a peculiar illustration. Your eyes are immediately drawn to it—it appears to be an illustrated schematic of a bullet trajectory.

"Good morning!" he says warmly. "So you two are the keen-eyed detectives who helped find one of Oswald's bullets? It's an honor to meet you. I've heard from Mr. Hoover that you both have the makings of fantastic investigators."

Specter then nods at you directly. "I even hear you've already solved one crime involving a little ballistics work—on the Billy Thompson shooting out at the Packard place in Dallas. Nice work, Detective!"

Wow! Word of your genius must be getting around! You can't help but beam with pride, replying, "Well, the angle of the entrance wound dictated the direction of the shot, Mr. Specter. It was actually pretty remedial work. But thanks."

Specter then gestures towards his illustration, saying, "In the case of the Kennedy shooting, we believe the bullet

you found, CE 399, entered the President's back, exited his throat, then struck Connally, breaking his rib, shattering his wrist, and finally coming to rest in his thigh."

Jenni lets out a gasp, finally replying, "Then it *fell* out onto the stretcher that Turtleneck here kicked? Without even a trace of *blood*? Excuse me, but that sounds idiotic!"

Specter offers a polite, understanding nod, then takes a breath, "Well, with all due respect, honey, stranger things have happened. And I'm not sure you're really an expert on the finer points of ballistic science."

He then leans towards you, smiling. "We've already consulted with some of the finest ballistic scientists in the country, and they agree this is what took place. Now we'd love to involve you both in our investigation, but only if you're willing to support our findings. So, are you, son?"

If you answer, "That sounds ... plausible," turn to page *100.*

If you reply, "I'll believe your magic bullet nonsense when I see it with my own eyes!", turn to page *104.*

"Sorry, Jenni," you reply, slipping the bullet into an evidence bag you conveniently keep in your pocket, "but this is a state investigation into a murder! This bullet goes back to the DPD."

She shakes her head, then punches you on the shoulder with a jocular smile, saying, "Suit yourself, Turtleneck. I know what a stickler you are for procedure."

Jenni then turns and glides over to a nearby FBI agent. She whispers something to him. His face darkens—and he storms angrily over to you, extending his massive palm.

"Turn it over, kid," he growls.

You shoot Jenni an exasperated look, which she dismisses with a disarming shrug.

"I'm sorry, sir," you answer back boldly, "but I'm a detective with the Dallas Police Department. And the feds don't have *any* juristiction over our investigation."

He considers your point carefully, then, with a lightning flash of his arm, he pistol whips you in the face repeatedly! *Bam! Bam! Bam!*

You crumple into a pathetic ball on the floor, your mouth swelling with blood. He then rummages through your pockets, fishing out the evidence bag.

"Thanks for your cooperation, son," he mutters as he walks away.

You try to protest, but find it's hard to talk, now that you're missing so many teeth.

YOU LOSE

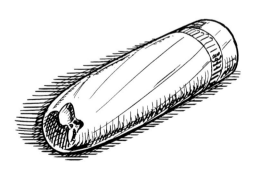

This film proves Kennedy was shot from the front, and not by Oswald! you tell yourself. *The American people have to be shown the truth, not just told about it!*

Summoning all your courage, you pull the reel off the projector and stuff it down the front of your pants.

You race towards the exit, and are just about to clear the door when suddenly, you find yourself running smack dab into the chest of a strapping Secret Service agent!

"What's the hurry, son?" he growls menacingly, eyeing you suspiciously.

Yikes! You'll have to think of something fast!

If you tell him, "I've got to go to the bathroom, now!", turn to page 93.

If you tell him, "I've got to get to home, I've got a hot date with a cool chick named Jenni!", turn to page 93.

If you tell him, "I've got to catch Dan Rather, he ran off and left his Brylcreem!", turn to page 93.

If you tell him, "I've stolen evidence of other shooters in Dealey Plaza and have to share it with the American people immediately so that a proper investigation can take place, and not this travesty of justice that's unfolding on TV!", turn to page 106.

Though the detective in you is tempted to steal this obvious proof of a frontal shot for the public good, you resist the urge, trusting that Dan Rather will disclose the truth of another shooter to the world. You race home and rush to the living room to find your mother watching the news tearfully.

"Mom! Turn it to CBS! You won't believe what Dan Rather and I just saw—and he's about to tell America what REALLY happened in Dealey Plaza!"

"What is it, son?" she asks breathlessly as she changes the channel. "What did you see?"

But no sooner has she changed the channel than Dan Rather's somber face fills it—he's starting!

"The films we saw were captured by an amateur photographer," he says, grimly, "who had a particularly good vantage point, just past the building from which the fatal shot was fired."

Wait a minute ... what the heck's he talking about? That's not what happened!

"*Past the building from...?*" you respond. "*What--?!*" You're stunned, as Rather continues, reading from notes:

"In the next instant, with this time Mrs. Kennedy apparently looking on, a second shot hit the President's head. His head could be seen to move violently forward."

"What are you TALKING about?!" you scream in anger at the television. "He was hit from the front! We saw it together, you idiot!"

Your mother grows pale. "What are you saying, son?"

You shake your head in violent disbelief, "Mom, Mom, he's wrong—or he's lying! We watched the film together! Kennedy was shot from the *front*—we saw him go backwards! There's no mistaking it! Whoever shot him, they must've been behind the fence in Dealey!"

Your mother places her hand on your knee. "Are you absolutely sure, son?"

"I'd bet my life on it, Mom," you answer. "I just don't know why he'd lie about it."

"Because he was told to," she replies hopelessly.

Go on to the next page.

If your faith in the Fourth Estate hadn't already been shaken enough, it's completely destroyed only days later, when Life Magazine publishes stills from the Zapruder film.

Thirty-one photo enlargements from the film are presented in sequence to simulate playback. But your keen detective eye notes that where the deadly shot occurs, the frames have been sequenced incorrectly, to create the illusion of Kennedy's head going forward, not back. What you earlier ascribed to journalistic incompetence is clearly something far worse. It's malice! Rather than aiding in the investigation of a crime, the media is abetting the cover-up.

You find yourself wondering whether the now-silenced Oswald had *anything* to do with the murder of JFK. Even if he did, you *know* he couldn't have acted alone, despite everything the media is reporting.

Whoever *really* killed JFK must have a lot of friends in high places. They didn't just get away with murder. They got away with the cover-up, too. Too bad you weren't a good enough detective to uncover it!

YOU LOSE

It's a bright spring morning, and you're standing on the steps of the Lincoln Memorial on a picture-perfect summer day. You can hardly believe your eyes as you gaze out into the crowd—hundreds of thousands of your grateful countrymen, holding signs and waving flags. And they've all come to see YOU—the brilliant kid detective who risked all to solve the most impenetrable murder in history!

You unravelled a conspiracy so complex, it tied rogue CIA agents with vengeful Mafia dons, angry Cuban exiles, duplicitous FBI agents, greedy munitions builders, Texas oilmen, disinfo specialists, and countless others! The Feds even had to build a new prison just to house them all. In a poignant irony, they called it the JFK Memorial Prison!

The shocking revelations shook the country to its core, but today, Americans are celebrating. The crowd roars as President Robert F. Kennedy walks onto the dais. He grasps your hand, and whispers "Thank you, son," before placing the Presidential Medal of Freedom around your neck. He steps to the microphone and clears his throat.

"My fellow Americans," he says, in his Boston Irish accent, "today we are gathered to honor the bravery and dedication of this outstanding young man. Because of this boy's extraordinary courage, we can now say that never again will murderers and traitors be allowed to escape justice with impunity. We can rest easy, knowing that the myriad evildoers who murdered my brother and attempted to destroy our democracy itself are now in prison, and will never again be free to unleash their terror on our nation!"

The applause is deafening! You feel a hand on your shoulder. It's Jackie Kennedy, and she's crying. "Thank you," she says. As you embrace her, you gaze out over her shoulder, to the crowd gathered before you. You see Americans of every race, every age, every income level, all cheering for you. In the distance, the sun shines on the Washington Monument. It's a beautiful morning in the greatest country in the world, a nation with liberty and justice for all, such as it always was, and, thanks to the courage and honor of people like you, such as it always will be.

YOU WIN!

84

Your urine-soaked sheets can wait—there's a crime to solve! You change clothes, then bike straight back to the police station. But to your dismay, the FBI has taken over! They're putting all the evidence on a plane and shipping it to DC. Even worse, they seem even more eager to pin all the blame on Oswald than the Dallas cops were! You try to interest them in witness reports of shooters behind the Plaza fence and witness tampering. But nobody cares.

"Stay out of the way," one grim-faced fed tells you, "or we'll arrest you for interfering in a federal investigation."

Defeated, you retire to your father's office. As you sit down, dejected, you noticed a handwritten note on his desk.

> Chief:
> We got two calls last night you should be aware of. One to Sheriff McCoy (2:15 am), the other to Lieutenant Grammer (3:00 am). Both times the (same?) caller said Oswald dies in the basement tomorrow during the move to county jail—unless we change things up. You may want extra protection.
> Alveeta [172]

It's just as you feared! You have no idea who killed JFK, but it's obvious Oswald is being set up to take all the blame, even for things he couldn't possibly have done. Suddenly, the door opens! It's your father—and he looks as relieved as you do worried. But before you can tell him of the death threats, his phone rings. He picks it up.

"Hello? Oh, hey, honey," he says, then his eyes bulge. "What? Are you serious? Well, yes, of course, dear..."

He puts down the phone and looks at you, mystified.

"That was your mother," he says, looking stupefied. "She wants you off the case, and home. *Now.* Apparently, somebody peed in your bed last night? But who would *do* that? Ugh, another mystery to solve! When does it end?"

What an idiot! You don't know what's worse, your shame at wetting the bed, or being the spawn of the world's dumbest detective. But either way, you're off the case. And you're in big trouble. Urine big trouble, indeed!

YOU LOSE

You decide you should probably go ahead and change your pee-stained sheets before you leave. After all, you don't want your mom to think you've started wetting the bed again like a baby!

You begin pulling off the wet, yellow sheets and crumpling them into a ball. But before you can finish the job, you hear the door creaking open behind you!

"Just a second, Mom!" you say, as you scrunch up the sheets tightly. Ugh! You really soaked them good!

"Hey, Turtleneck!" a voice from behind says.

Drat! It's Jenni Mudd! Your longtime rival in detective work! *And she's in your bedroom!*

You try to turn as nonchalantly as possible as she continues talking. She says with a bright smile, "Your mom said I could ... come up ... and..."

Her eyes narrow as she examines the ball of bed dressing in your hands. She raises a curious eyebrow, then asks, "So, what are you doing?"

You can see the wheels turning in *her* keen detective mind! *Double-drat!* You'll have to think fast! You're not sure, but you think she might have caught a glimpse of the yellow stains on your sheets. Or did she?

If you say, "Oh, nothing. I'm about to go back up to the station and solve the crime", turn to page 108.

If you reply, "Ugh. I'm doing the laundry. My dog peed on my bed again", turn to page 110.

"Absolutely, Jenni," you answer. "Hoover promised me a real job as an investigator—then rewarded me with an empty title and a glorified secretary's job!"

"I wouldn't say it's *glorified*," she replies with a smirk, "but I take your point. Come on, we've got a plane to catch."

Wow! You can't believe Jenni's actually turning against the FBI on this one. But you couldn't be more excited to be back on the case, even at this late date!

You get up, dropping your "Junior Detective" plaque in the trash. It's time to be a REAL detective again!

In a matter of hours, you've packed a week's supply of clothing—every turtleneck you own—and are racing through the Dallas night with Jenni in a taxi to the Love Field airport.

Your heart is pounding in your chest like a jackrabbit! Your hands tremble. To your shock, Jenni takes one of them into hers, and says gently, "Calm down, Turtleneck. You look like you're about to have a heart attack."

You turn to look at her, surprised by her touch. As the streetlights race by, they cast a lovely glow on her face. You've never really noticed it before, but she's actually a rather beautiful girl, in her snotty, know-it-all way. She smiles at you with surprising tenderness, then reaches into her purse. To your shock, she pulls out a silver flask.

"Here," she says, opening it, "It'll take the edge off ..."

She puts it to her lips and takes a swig, then hums in satisfaction. She then hands it to you expectantly.

You raise it in an impromptu toast, then say, "To us, cracking *The Case of The Mind Controlled Assassin!*"

Though you've never had a sip of alcohol in your life, you take a swig—and a big one, too—to show her she's not the only one who knows how to drink like a grown-up!

Go on to the next page.

It burns like acid going down your throat. Jenni keeps smiling at you, so beautifully. And yet ... now it's two smiles? Then it's three. Suddenly, the whole world feels like it's spinning! Stars flash across your eyes and you struggle just to stay upright! Is this an allergic reaction?

"Jenni, help!" you gasp. "I need ... I need ... a hospital ..."

She nods, and then, to your surprise, she spits out *her* swig on the cab floor, replying, almost sadly, "Don't worry, Turtleneck. We're going to a hospital, remember?"

And then suddenly, everything goes black.

Turn to page 88.

Jenni is gone. And so is reality itself. You spend days in a dreamworld—*or are they years?* Images flutter through your mind but refuse explanation.

The beautiful nurse in a polka dot dress ... *but what is she injecting you with?*

A black football helmet strapped over your head ... *but why does it leave you in darkness?*

The endless tape loops ... *but what are they saying?*

In this never-ending haze, you can hardly commit a thought to memory. Your consciousness feels melted. Everything within it mixes together and loses form. Nothing endures beyond a moment.

But one scene persists over all, clear as a morning sun.

It's the end of the day. You see a bright yellow sunflower before you. The nurse whispers into your ear, "It's time to water your flower." And water it you do. You squeeze the trigger, spraying out gentle blasts until the bottle is emptied.

"You've done a wonderful job," the nurse says lovingly. "You're almost ready, Detective."

And then it starts all over again. Injections. Helmets. Tape loops. You're watering your flower. Injections. Helmets. Tape loops. You're watering your flower. Injections. Helmets. Tape loops. You're watering your flower.

Only it's not a flower anymore ...

Go on to the next page.

You emerge from your nearly endless haze to a terrifying sight. It's not your flower you're standing in front of, but a man. And with every squeeze of the trigger, you've fired another bullet—until you've emptied the chamber!

Chaos explodes all around you! Men jump you from all sides, punching you and grabbing at your pistol. And the nurse in the polka dot dress has vanished into the crowd.

You're smashed to the ground, pinned face down by strong and furious men. But on the floor not far from you, you see something that fills you with absolute horror.

It's Robert F. Kennedy! He's been shot! *BY YOU!!!*

After an eternity spent in a mindless haze, you feel your wits coming back to you, bringing with them the horrifying realization of what has just taken place. You wanted to know if the CIA could really create an unwitting assassin. Now you have your answer. And you'd give anything—including your very life—if you could only unlearn that terrible lesson.

YOU LOSE

"Sorry, Jenni," you reply coolly. "It's tempting, but I made a deal with J. Edgar Hoover and—"

She interrupts with a belly laugh, "And he's rewarded you with a job taking phone messages for Lupe The Janitor! You got scammed, ya dork! I'm giving you a chance to still be a real detective—not a sellout!"

It hurts to hear her say it, but you stay firm. "Sorry. But a deal's a deal. Good luck with your lead. I'd rather be loyal."

Jenni shrugs, then says, "Suit yourself, Turtleneck. I'll solve it without you!"

And with that, she's gone. If she learns anything about mind-controlled CIA assassins, she doesn't tell you about it.

•

A few weeks later, Hoover himself barges into your office. You're shocked—and even more so when he gives you a huge bear hug!

"Son," he booms out, "you've proven a valuable asset to the FBI! You're loyal, diligent, you do what you're told, you don't get distracted, and you don't ask questions! Just what we look for in a senior federal investigator!"

"But sir," you reply, "I'm only a junior detective."

"Not anymore, son!" he laughs. "I'm promoting you! Welcome to the big leagues, my boy!"

Zowie! What amazing news! It's incredible what a little loyalty can buy a guy, and in your case, it buys you plenty! Hoover gives you a new office, a huge salary, and then he puts you to work on REAL investigations for a change!

Oh, sure, sometimes it feels like you're being asked to ignore critical clues and facts. And yeah, occasionally you're expressly told to destroy evidence that contradicts a predetermined FBI conclusion. But that's a small sacrifice to make—and it's all in the interest of the greater good, right? After all, sometimes, the interests of national security have to come before fact-finding, right? And that's a small price to pay for the luxury of being a bona fide federal G-man!

Turn to page 92.

Over the next many years, you distinguish yourself from your FBI peers with your exemplary service to the Bureau. You practically *live* at the FBI now. And Hoover rewards that loyalty with *more* money, perks, and responsibility!

So it's hardly a surprise when your phone rings in the early hours of June 5, 1968. It's Director Hoover—and he sounds as serious as a heart attack.

"Son, we need your help," he begins. "Senator Robert Kennedy was just gunned down at the Ambassador Hotel in Los Angeles ... I want you on my red eye tonight, to aid the LAPD and our FBI field office in this investigation."

Deep in the recesses of your mind, a muted voice speaks. Some girl you once knew. Her crazy brainwashed assassin theory. But you ignore it, as usual. Kid stuff. Nothing more.

Hoover continues: "Lot of confusion down there needs clearing up. Lot of crazy theories. Girls in polka-dotted dresses ... multiple shooters ... bunch of nonsense, as usual."

You finally allow yourself to ask, "So, who did it, Sir?"

He repies mechanically, "Insane assassin. America-hater. Acting alone. You know the drill."

Oh yes. You know it *very* well by now.

YOU LOSE

Thinking fast, you start to spit out your excuse.

"I've got to—" you start to reply, but before you can get another word out, he's got a massive hand right down the front of your pants!

"Well what do we have here?" he says darkly, pulling out the reel of film. "You were just going to walk out of here with this, huh? You know that's a felony offense, right?"

You start to reply, but he barely lets you get a word out.

"You hiding anything else down there?" he says, reaching once again down the front of your pants.

"No! No, sir!" you manage to reply. "I promise!"

Suddenly, you feel his beefy hand grabbing you right in your no-no zone! He squeezes like he's crushing walnuts!

ARGH!

You crumple to the floor, paralyzed by the electric pain that radiates out in all directions from your tenders! The air is squeezed completely from your lungs in an endless groan. You've never felt a pain so intense, so consuming, and find yourself curling reflexively into a fetal position.

Through a hazy curtain of shooting stars of agony, you see him slide the reel into the breast pocket of his suit.

"I'm going to let you off with a warning," he says with a shrug, and a smile. He leaves the room.

YOU LOSE

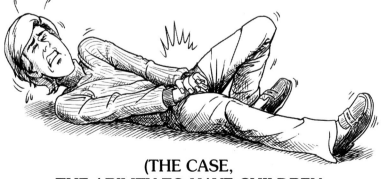

**(THE CASE,
THE ABILITY TO HAVE CHILDREN
AND THE WILL TO LIVE)**

Intrigued by the possibility of an alien connection, you turn to Coppens and say, "Professor, what's this alien connection you were talking about?"

Professor Coppens smiles widely, speaking in a raspy voice. "In July of 1947, the United States government recovered a crashed flying saucer just north of Roswell, New Mexico. It contained corpses of *non-human origin*! In the years that followed, more and more sightings of unidentified flying objects were reported—and more spacecraft, and aliens, were recovered and spirited off to Area 51 in southern Nevada for further study."

"What on Earth do UFOs have to do with the Kennedy assassination?" you reply skeptically.

"Perhaps the better question is '*What OFF Earth?*', my boy!" he titters in amusement. "You see, these aliens began visiting us after we detonated the first atomic bomb. They were worried, you see, that with this Promethean fire we might destroy ourselves—as so many other alien civilizations have before us! They came in peace, to protect us from ourselves!"

Angelo moans in annoyance, "Oh, come on, Coppens! This is idiotic!"

But the Professor continues, even more excitedly. "Eventually, a top secret meeting between these aliens and members of our government took place. A treaty was signed—allowing *them* to conduct human experimentation and *us* access to some of their most powerful technology! When President Kennedy was briefed on this incredible news, he wanted to reveal it to the world! Imagine how it could've changed things. It could end war itself! But of course, that's why the military-industrial complex killed him!"

Agent Joab shakes his head. "No, Professor. This is childish CIA disinformation. Your sources—"

"*My sources worked alongside me on the Manhattan Project!*" he barks in reply. "These are men of science! And of peace!"

The Professor produces a photo—a strange, greenish-grey humanoid with huge dark eyes. It looks alive!

"Waiting inside Hangar 13 is the secret Kennedy died for. A living alien being from the Zeta Reticuli star system," he continues, placing a hand on your shoulder. "If one of us could sneak inside, capture it, and reveal it to the world, then perhaps Kennedy will not have died in vain."**176**

You can't help but remain skeptical—it sounds so crazy! Yet the photo looks so convincing. The alien really looks alive—and like it's peering into your soul. Could this *really* be the reason Kennedy died?

If you decide to go to Hangar 13 to investigate further, turn to page 114.

If you ask Angelo about his Mafia theory, turn to page 98.

If you ask Agent Joab about his CIA theory, turn to page 96.

You turn to Agent Joab and ask, "You were an intelligence agent, right? Do you *really* think one of your guys could've killed the President of the United States?"

Agent Joab takes a deep breath, his eyes tearing up shamefully. "I don't think, son. I *know*."

"When I joined the Special Intelligence Group, I was a bright-eyed boy not much older than you," he continues. "I believed America was the land of the free and home of the brave, and I'd be danged if I was going to let a bunch of godless Russian KGB agents crack the secret code of the whale songs before we did."

"But it wasn't long before I learned that other intelligence work was a far dirtier business than I signed up for. I'd been reassigned to report to Kermit Roosevelt, Jr., who headed up a CIA program called 'Operation Ajax.' Our assignment? Overthrow Mohammed Mosaddegh—the Prime Minister of Iran—and stop Iran from nationalizing their oil industry. We paid thugs—gangsters, killers, even Nazis—to stage riots and murder civilians, and replaced a democratically elected leader with a despotic puppet, the Shah of Iran, all to guarantee America a slice of the Iranian oil revenues!"

A single tear rolls from his dark eyes down his cheek. He puts a hand on your shoulder, squeezing it gently. "I resigned that very day, and made a promise to myself. I'd never sit idly by and watch my own brothers in the spy game overthrow a government. Not in Chile. Not in Vietnam. And certainly not in the United States of America."

He waves the police reports you retrieved from evidence control, then smiles. "Son, with these reports, we can call a press conference tomorrow and prove that Oswald couldn't have acted alone." He taps his temple, then continues, "I know *exactly* how the CIA pulled this off—and more importantly, I know *why*."

Vivalzi finally breaks her silence, "It's proof that others were involved—but it's not enough, Joab! Plus, you defected from the CIA—you've got skeletons in your closet. They'll paint you as a rogue agent with Communist ties, or worse!"

Agent Joab nods, then turns to you soberly. "I'm willing to have my character assassinated, Vivalzi, if that's what it takes to get the media's attention. It's a small price to pay to crack this case open. I'm willing to name names—and when I do, it'll be impossible for them to pin it on Oswald alone."

Dr. Vivalzi's face suddenly brightens. She turns to you with a beatific smile. "Wait a minute! You're the police chief's son—you've solved *countless* crimes! And America *loves* boy detectives! *You* could lead the conference! You could tell them that you saw evidence destruction underway, and you stopped it—and demand the evidence be opened to the public! You don't have any secrets to hide, right?"

"Well," you reply, "I may have slipped Slugs O'Toole a bar of chocolate laxatives once, to solve *The Case of the Antique Ring.* But I just *knew* he swallowed that ring! And that afternoon in the school bathroom, I got the proof!"

Everyone in the room bursts into sudden guffaws.

"Son," Agent Joab chuckles, "If that's the worst they've got on you, you'll be A-OK. So make the choice—if you want me to lead this press conference, I'm happy to do it. But if you'd rather take point, feel free. Either way, the truth comes out. This was a conspiracy. And when we prove it, America will demand the evidence—*all of it*—be released."

What a choice! You've no doubt that Agent Joab knows details you'd never know about government overthrows and spycraft. But on the other hand, Vivalzi's right. America loves kid detectives, and if you choose to break the story, you just might go down in history as one of the greats!

If you ask Agent Joab to lead a press conference about CIA involvement in the killing, turn to page 116.

If you decide to lead it yourself, turn to page 122.

If you ask Professor Coppens about his Area 51 theory, turn to page 94.

If you ask Angelo about his Mafia theory, turn to page 98.

You ask Angelo to tell you more about the Mafia angle.

He smiles. "It's real simple, kid. The Mob helped get Kennedy elected. They stole the West Virginia primary for him, then delivered him the votes of a bunch of corpses to put him over the top in Illinois. Then the CIA got the Mob involved in their plans to kill Castro. Am I wrong, Joab?"

Joab lets a deep, frustrated sigh. "No, but—"

Angelo keeps talking. "So how did JFK reward them for their help? He made his brother Robert the Attorney General, and they both declared war on organized crime! The Kennedys even deported New Orleans Mafia boss Carlos Marcello. Feds kidnapped him, and dumped him right on a beach in Guatemala in '61!"

"But what does Oswald have to do with this?" you reply, baffled. "Sergeant Fanucci said he was a *Communist*."

"*Fanucci?*", he says, exasperated, "He's just another Mob-connected cop in Dallas, kid! And Oswald? His uncle 'Dutz' was a bookie for Marcello. Oswald grew up in New Orleans, and was pals with a psycho named David Ferrie, one of Marcello's lackeys. It was Ferrie who flew Marcello back to the US. And from what *I* hear, they talked about the JFK hit all the way back, and how to pin it on Oswald."

Joab can take no more. "Oswald is an *intelligence* agent, Angelo! In deep cover!"

Angelo nods in agreement, exclaiming, "Exactly! You think the CIA is going to let that come out, Joab? Course not. They gotta keep up the ruse. If the American people found out Kennedy's suspected assassin was a CIA asset, it'd be the end of the Agency. He's the perfect Mafia patsy!"

"But wouldn't the FBI—" you start to ask.

"FBI won't *touch* the Mob, kid!" he laughs. "They got pics of J. Edgar doing the dirty with another man!"

Zowie! It sounds like the Mafia had a great motive to kill JFK, and maybe even the means to blackmail the CIA and FBI into a cover-up, but still, it all seems so circumstantial!

"I don't know, Angelo," you reply hesitantly. "We can't build a case on sexual blackmail, unsavory relatives, and hearsay about Mafia payback. We need evidence!"

"Course you do," he says. "That's why you gotta get to Ferrie, kid." He hands you a mugshot of Ferrie— a menacing looking guy with painted-on eyebrows and an obvious wig— then continues. "This is him, kid. Get a confession from him, this whole charade crashes down! He was just in a courtroom in New Orleans with Marcello himself. My sources say he's on his way to the Alamont Hotel in Houston right now. We put you on a bus, you're there in three hours!"

Hmmm. It still seems like a long shot. But then again, the Mafia *is* notoriously brutal, secretive, and vindictive. Maybe they did have a hand in this? You'd have to track down this David Ferrie character to find out!

If you decide to go to Houston to track down David Ferrie, turn to page 128.

If you ask Professor Coppens about his Area 51 theory, turn to page 94.

If you ask Agent Joab about his CIA theory, turn to page 96.

Even though you find Specter's single-bullet theory completely ludicrous, you agree to go along with it.

"I'll help the Commission prove this," you say with an uneasy shrug. "It's for the good of the country, right?"

"Absolutely!" Specter says, handing you the rifle. "Now, go shoot some cadavers!"

And shoot some cadavers you do! Working with a team of four ballistics experts, you shoot hundreds of bullets into goat and human cadavers, including ten shots into the wrists of corpses to simulate Connally's wrist-shattering wound.

All of your test bullets suffer severe mutilations. The noses all flatten and twist terribly. Not one of them survives in the pristine shape of Exhibit 399—the bullet that supposedly created seven wounds between JFK and Connally. And though three out of four of Specter's ballistics experts reject his single-bullet conclusion, you cast your lot with Dr. Alfred Oliver, the lone supporter.

"It's for the good of the country," you tell yourself again, trying to will yourself to believe it.

When the Warren Commission report is released, it ignores the dissenting majority of its own experts and claims the "ballistic tests support the conclusions of Governor Connally's doctors that all his wounds were caused by one bullet." You know it's a lie, but what choice did they have? If they admitted to more bullets, they'd have to admit to additional shooters, too. But that would mean a conspiracy killed Kennedy—and some of the bad guys got away with it.

If they get away with it, it's because people like you helped cover it up with idiotic lies about magic bullets! your conscience barks in rebuke.

But over time, with considerable effort, you learn to ignore that voice. For the good of the country.

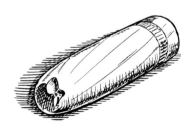

Go on to the next page.

Time passes quickly in the years after you help pin Kennedy's death solely on Oswald and his magic bullet. The war in Vietnam that JFK hoped to end expands greatly under his replacement, LBJ. Even you don't escape its reach. Drafted in '66, you take a paralyzing bullet to the spine fighting in Khe Sanh less than a year later! *Drat!*

In early '68, JFK's brother Robert begins running for President and campaigning against the Vietnam War. But no sooner had he begun to campaign than he, too, was assassinated—by yet another crazy lone gunman.

The assassin, Sirhan Sirhan, proved to be an even more magical shooter than Oswald. He fired his shots while standing three feet in front of RFK, but the coroner declared the fatal shots were fired from only inches *behind Robert Kennedy's head!* They found powder burns behind his ears. Even more incredibly, the purported assassin fired at least ten shots from a pistol that only held eight bullets, hitting RKF four times and five other people, one of them twice! And the Vietnam War that RFK hoped to bring to an end as President drags on for another seven agonizing years, nearly bankrupting the country. *Zowie!*

Even a morally-compromised intellectual sellout like yourself can't help but be wracked with guilt. It hangs over you like a sword as the next decades of your life fly by, and the power and influence of the war industry grows ever more ubiquitous.

Turn to page 102.

102

Nearly sixty years later, your life is nearly at an end. Your children followed your compromised example, never learning about character or sacrifice or taking hard stands. When you become too old to care for yourself, they dump you in a retirement home and wait for you to die so they can fight over their paltry inheritance.

Yet your mind never dulls. Your wits stay as sharp as they were in your brighter days as a promising kid detective, even as your body begins to decline.

Day after day, you're a prisoner of cable news, alertly piecing together the slow-motion decline of the country you once so patriotically loved. The war industry, among so many self-interested corporate powers, feasts upon the bloated, swollen budgets of the federal government. Corrupt politicians now openly take bribes from big business to steer corporate welfare towards yet another lined coffer. No President bothers to stand up to the brazen criminality of it all. Few have had the guts—not since it became clear how disposable even Presidents can be, and how easily the absurdities of their obvious conspiratorial deaths can be covered-up by willing lackeys like Arlen Specter. *And you.* Yet you know, as surely as JFK wasn't killed by a magic bullet, that the State of the Union is unsustainable. The only question on your sharp mind is: *How long can it last?*

And one afternoon, in December of 2019, you get your answer. The hyperinflation that began in 2017 has prompted riots throughout America. Within two years, the Joint Chiefs have had enough, and they declare martial law!

You watch the scene in DC unfold on your giant TV screen. The Department of Homeland Security rolls tanks into every major city. You hear an explosion in the distance.

"My God!" screams an elderly woman in a hallway. "Tanks! There's tanks in the streets! Of America! *Whyyyyy?!*"

Unlike so many others around you, you *know* the answer. And the fear grips you so tightly, your bladder gives way. It's only a matter of time before your bowels follow.

YOU LOSE

Or, if you decide to page a nurse- turn to page 130.

You rebuke Specter harshly, "With all due respect, sir, Jenni's right—this is completely idiotic! How could one bullet cause all those wounds? And emerge unscathed? Only a fool could believe such nonsense! This sounds like a cover-up, plain and simple. And if you and your Freemasonic buddies think you're going to get away with it—"

Specter breaks into a horrifying smile. Then he jumps up, revealing he's wearing a Freemasonic ritual apron! *174*

He then begins moving his left hand and speaking in some mystic language you can't identify! Sparks seem to fly from his wriggling fingers. Then, to your horror, he levels Oswald's rifle at you and pulls the trigger!

You feel the agonizing pain as the bullet rips through your back and explodes out your chest! Then it seems to hover a moment—*or is it just your panicked imagination run wild?*—as it continues towards Jenni at blinding speed, entering her side, then piercing her front with an unmistakable crack of bone! It shatters her wrist, and buries itself in her thigh!

You both slump to the ground, wracked with unbelievable pain and terror!

Arlen Specter approaches your bleeding, broken bodies with a calm, deliberate smile, once again the portrait of lawyerly serenity.

He leans over your gasping, terrified faces, then says, "I've got good news, and I've got bad news, kids."

"The good news is," he continues, "neither of your wounds are fatal."

He picks up the bullet that mysteriously fell out of Jenni's thigh, and holds it up for you both to inspect. It's in pristine condition, without a drop of blood on it!

Then he chuckles, reaching slowly into his Masonic apron pocket with his free hand. He pulls out two additional bullets, and quietly loads them into the rifle.

He then lowers the barrel right to your forehead and clears his throat.

"The bad news is ..."

BANG!

You never hear him finish explaining what the bad news was, but you have a pretty good guess.

YOU LOSE

Despite your intimidation, you step boldly forward and tell the Secret Service agent, "I'm taking this filmed evidence on behalf of the American people, sir. It proves there were other shooters in Dealey Plaza on Friday. The shot that killed the President came from the front, not behind—despite this farce of an investigation that's unfolding on television! And if you have one scrap of honor left in you, sir, you will help me do this! You swore an oath to protect him in life—to take a bullet for him if duty asked it. Won't you at least help me protect him in death?"

You brace yourself—expecting the worst. But the mask of intimidation on his face melts away, and to your shock, you see a single tear roll down his cheek.

In a quiet voice, he replies, "We shouldn't have stayed out last night. We went to Fort Worth, we drank too much. We, we had firemen watching the Presidential Suite at the hotel, for God's sake!"

Suddenly, he starts sobbing! Unbelievable!

With his head hung in shame, his voice faltering, he continues, "I never liked the man. But you're right, son—I swore an oath to protect him. And I failed to honor it."

You place a comforting hand on his shoulder, "It's not too late. Help me honor him now. Let me take this evidence and reveal it. Before it gets buried under a mountain of lies."

He looks at you through red-rimmed eyes for a small eternity. Then, without a word, he nods, giving you his blessing to leave.

You turn to leave, rushing towards the exit.

Go on to the next page.

You race towards the exit and are just about to clear the door, when suddenly you find yourself running smack dab into the chest of ANOTHER strapping Secret Service agent!

"What's the rush, kid?" he growls menacingly.

"I'm taking this film," you boldly reply, tapping the bulge in your crotch, "with the blessing of your fellow agent."

"The hell you are!"

Suddenly, he shoves a massive hand down the front of your pants and pulls out the reel. You try to grab it back, and get a lightning fast knee to the crotch for your efforts.

ARGH!

You crumple to the floor, paralyzed by the electric pain that radiates out in all directions from your tenders! The air is squeezed completely from your lungs in an endless groan! You've never felt a pain so intense, so consuming, and find yourself curling reflexively into a fetal position.

Through a hazy curtain of shooting stars of agony, you see him slide the reel into the breast pocket of his suit.

"You're under arrest for evidence tampering," he says, as he bends over your crumpled, agonized mass and slaps you in cuffs.

YOU LOSE

**(YOUR FREEDOM, THE CASE,
THE ABILITY TO HAVE CHILDREN
AND THE WILL TO LIVE)**

You decide to bluff.

"What am *I* doing, Jenni? I'm heading back to the police station to work the case! What are *you* doing?"

Jenni shrugs, then asks, "Can I work it with you?"

With the memory of last night's pee-inducing nightmare still fresh in your mind, and Jenni's dreamy delight in your dream death, you decide maybe your subconscious knows something you don't yet. You shake your head.

"Sorry, Jenni," you say. "I think we should work alone."

She sighs, disappointed, then says, "Fair enough, Turtleneck. May the best detective win." She leaves.

You throw your urine-soaked sheets in the washing machine on the way out, and start a wash to destroy any evidence of your crime. Then you throw on a clean turtleneck and pants, and bike straight back to police headquarters.

But to your dismay, the FBI and Secret Service have taken over. They're putting all the evidence on a plane and shipping it to DC! Even worse, they seem even more eager to pin all the blame on Oswald than the Dallas cops were! You try to interest them in reports of shooters behind the Plaza fence and witness tampering. But nobody cares.

"Stay out of the way," one grim-faced agent tells you, "Or we'll arrest you for interfering in a federal investigation."

Defeated, you retire to your father's office. As you sit down, dejected, you noticed a handwritten note on his desk.

Go on to the next page.

Chief:
We got two calls last night you should be aware of. One to Sheriff McCoy (2:15 am), the other to Lieutenant Grammer (3:00 am). Both times the (same?) caller said Oswald dies in the basement tomorrow during the move to county jail—unless we change things up. You may want extra protection.

Alveeta [172]

It's just as you feared! You have no idea who killed JFK, but it's obvious Oswald is being set up to take all the blame, even for things he couldn't possibly have done. Suddenly, the door opens. It's your father—and he looks as relieved as you do worried.

"Dad, did you see this?" you ask, holding up the note. "You got multiple death threats against Oswald last night!"

He waves it off, "Ahh—probably just cranks."

"But why take any chances, Dad?" you ask. "At least give him extra protection in the basement. Just trust me."

But your father isn't buying it. If Oswald's going to get any extra protection tomorrow, it's going to have to come from you.

If you decide to help escort Oswald tomorrow, turn to page 132.

If you decide to trust your father's instincts, turn to page 136.

"Oh, nothing," you reply with a casual shrug. "My dog Muffin, she sleeps on my bed sometimes. And last night, I guess she decided to relieve herself, too."

Jenni laughs, and offers a commiserating nod. "Yeah, our dog J. Edgar just goes wherever he wants, too."

You laugh back as you unobtrusively drop the sheets into your dirty clothes bin. "You named your dog after the Director of the FBI?"

She replies, "Yeah. My dad says they both poop wherever they want and let other people clean up after!"

She bought it! Maybe she's not as smart as you thought!

You let out a big laugh, intrigued by the implications. Maybe Lee Harvey Oswald's note to the FBI is yet *another* mess Hoover expects other people to clean up?

Jenni then shrugs and says, "Well, why don't I wait for you downstairs? But hurry up, OK? You won't *believe* what I learned at Dealey yesterday. I was telling my dad about it; he said I could write a book! He knows people in publishing, and they *love* kid detective stories! Imagine!"

She then gives you a smug smile and slips back out.

A book deal? Oh, no! If she gets one of those, she'll never let you hear the end of it!

You finish getting ready, and are about to head downstairs when you remember the dirty clothes bin.

Gotta keep the ruse up, you think, as you grab the dirty laundry bin.

When you make it back downstairs, you find your mother and Jenni talking on the couch in the living room.

Jenni notices you and smiles. You nod quietly back, heading straight to the laundry room to get rid of the incriminating evidence.

Go on to the next page.

"Son, come in here!" your mom shouts. "Jenni found some amazing clues in Dealey Plaza yesterday!"

"Sure, Mom, just let me drop this laundry in the wash!" you call back as you beeline to the washer and dryer.

You pull open the clothes washer and dump in your sheets. *Whew!* Case closed! You wash your hands in the kitchen sink, and head back to the living room.

Your mom shoots you a grateful smile. "So nice to have a little help on the laundry for a change!"

Uh-oh, she's at risk of blowing your cover!

Thinking fast, you shrug, "Well, Mom, I think Muffin did a little bit of *business* on my bed last night."

Your mom's expression becomes quizzical. "Really? *That's* strange, she's been—"

"So, Jenni!" you quickly interrupt. "Tell me about these clues you picked up."

Jenni's eyes narrow as she keys off your anxiety. "Sure. But do you mind if I meet Muffin first? I *do* love dogs so."

"Oh, of course, Jenni!" replies your mom. She turns and calls out in a clear, musical voice, "MUFF-in! Here, girl!"

You hear the telltale jingle of her aluminum collar tags as she rushes into the room and right up on your mother's lap. All five heaping pounds of her.

Jenni sidles up to her, scratching under her chin.

"Oh, I love chihuahuas!" she exclaims. "You're so tiny!"

Eager to shift her attentions back to her favorite subject, you ask, "So, Jenni. What's this I hear about a book deal?"

She stands up and says, "Yes, it's very exciting!" Then she remembers something. "Oh, can you hold that thought? I've got something I want to show you both."

Whew. Close call! She excuses herself and leaves the room. Your mom smiles at you warmly. "I know you're not her biggest fan, but I think she's a real doll! If you two got together, you might give birth to the next Sherlock Holmes!"

"*Ewww!*" you reply, to her guffaws.

Turn to page 112.

After a minute or so, Jenni returns to the living room. And to your absolute horror, she's got your balled-up bedsheets in her hand! OH, NO!

"Jenni!" your mom says sharply. "What on earth are you doing with my son's sheets?"

Jenni looks back at her apologetically. "I'm really sorry about this, ma'am, it's just that ... when he told me upstairs that his *dog* wet his bed, I didn't give it a second thought. But then I met Muffin—cute little Muffin—and wondered, *'Could such a tiny dog really do THIS?'"*

She opens the sheets—to reveal the gigantic pee stains that cover it from end nearly to end!

Your Mother gasps, horrified. "*Son!* Did you *really* try to frame sweet Muffin for one of your own misdeeds?"

This is worse than your nightmare! At least you DIED in that one!

"I'm sorry, Mom!" you reply in humiliation. "I had a nightmare—about JFK! All these disturbing clues! I must've wet the bed! And then Jenni came in and I panicked!"

As your mother glares at you, Jenni shoots you the smuggest look possible. Then she asks you, in an annoyingly sweet voice, "I know it's not really my place, but do you really think *you* should be investigating a murder, when you're so willing to frame innocents for crimes they didn't commit?"

Your mother nods resolutely, and replies, "She's absolutely right, son! If you can't be trusted with little things, then how can you be trusted with giant ones?"

And with that, you're off the case—AND grounded for a month! This couldn't possibly have turned out worse!

As you ruminate, humiliated, about this undignified end over the coming days, your keen detective mind can't help but wonder if YOU were another mess Hoover wanted cleaned up, and Jenni was the one doing the job for him!

YOU LOSE

Or, if you want to find out what came of Jenni's investigation, turn to page 138.

The professor's theory sounds crazy, but what if he's right? Is it possible President Kennedy was assassinated because he was about to tell the American people about secret alien treaties and aliens living at Area 51? It doesn't make much sense, but neither do those new "push-button" telephones you've been reading about—who knows what other weird, futuristic technologies the government has access to?

You decide you'd better check it out for yourself.

"I'll do it, Professor," you reply, "if you can get me to Nevada, that is."

He pulls a plane ticket from his jacket pocket, saying, "I was planning to go there myself this very day. But I'm old and weak, and my eyes are failing me. You go for me."

He drives you the short distance to Love Field, and wishes you luck as he hands you an envelope full of cash, "For cabs and such. Remember, the secrets are in Hangar 13. Ignore the rest!"

The flight to Las Vegas is nearly eight hours long, and you spend it mostly staring at the strange photo of the alien Dr. Coppens gave to you. You arrive that night, and find a hotel near the airport. You awake the next morning, ready for action, and are happy to see a cab conveniently parked in front of the hotel.

"Where to, bub?" the cabbie asks.

"Area 51," you reply casually, "Hangar 13."

He eyes you suspiciously for a moment, then replies, "You don't look much like the sort I take up there."

You hand him a small fortune—at least $20—and he smiles. "Next stop, Hangar 13!"

Two hours later, he's dropping you off on a dusty road in the middle of the Nevada desert. Once you rub the sand from your eyes, you can make out a series of large, light-colored structures in the distance. The biggest looks like a airplane hangar, with a small office building attached.

Go on to the next page.

As you hike towards the complex, you're surprised to see it's unguarded. There's a small sign in front, faded by the sun, that reads, "Hangar 13—OFFICIAL VISITORS ONLY —TRESPASSERS WILL BE SHOT ON SIGHT AND FINED." *Yikes!*

You skirt around the massive building, looking for an entrance. You spy a few small ground floor windows with open blinds. You peer into one. There's two men seated at a long table watching a TV in the corner. You see maps tacked up on the walls. Wait, what's that one? Houston Street, Commerce Street, Record Street. Zowie! You recognize the scene! It's Dealey Plaza!

On the television, Walter Cronkite reports the latest news. But you can't quite hear what he saying.

One of the men, dressed in a military uniform, loudly barks, "Yeah, well, serves the bastard right for saying we'd put a man on the moon in ten years!"

The other looks more like a scientist, and replies with a smile, "Oh, we'll put a man on the moon, sir. You can watch us do it on live TV. I just hope there's not an army of little green men waiting there for us."

They both laugh heartily at their strange, private joke and leave the room.

You're a little shaken. What could this mean?! You decide it's now or never—you've got to get in Hangar 13!

You continue your furtive sneaking around the building, and come to a giant metal door. A sign on it reads, "DO NOT ENTER." This must be it!

Suddenly, you hear footsteps. You peek around the corner, and see two armed guards. *Drat!* They've got 12-gauge shotguns, and are heading right toward you! You have time to run and hide behind that huge rock a few yards away, or you can take your chances inside the building. If it's unlocked, that is.

If you decide to run and hide behind the conveniently-placed rock, turn to page 131.

If you decide to go into the building, turn to page 142.

"Agent Joab," you reply, "Your knowledge of spycraft makes you a *much* better person to break this story. And I think America would be willing to forgive any past misdeeds you may have taken part in if you help expose this crime."

"Very well, son," Joab replies. "It will be my honor."

That afternoon, Vivalzi works the phones, calling every reporter in the Dallas-Fort Worth metroplex, excitedly telling them, "Tomorrow morning at 9:00, The Altair Society will break news of incredible developments in the assassination investigation!"

You even take a moment to call your rival, Jenni Mudd. Her mother answers the phone and informs you she's in Dealey Plaza, investigating the assassination herself. You reply, "Tell her not to bother. Tomorrow morning, we're cracking the case wide open!"

The next morning, it's showtime!

Agent Joab arrives, wearing his former spy uniform, a dashing black suit with white lapels. Dozens of reporters bark out questions. Jenni Mudd sits on the front row, looking anxious—no doubt at the prospects of being scooped!

Joab walks to the podium, raising his hands for silence.

"Ladies and gentlemen, yesterday afternoon, President Kennedy was gunned down in Dealey Plaza. Not, as you've been told, by Lee Harvey Oswald. But by a *conspiracy!*"

The crowd explodes with gasps, yelps and a deafening chorus of questions. His voice booms authoritatively over them all, "I know you have questions—*but let me speak!*"

When the noise dies down, he continues, "My name is McAdams. I was once a spy, my code name *Joab*, working for Allen Dulles' huge intelligence machine. At first, my work was innocent—helping my country beat the Russians in the Cold War race to crack the secrets of whale songs. But, to my eternal shame, I later had a hand in dirtier spy work—including the overthrow of governments. Ladies and gentlemen, what happened yesterday was a textbook *coup d'etat*, conducted by agents of the American CIA working most certainly under the direction of Allen Dulles himself! But this conspiracy goes even higher than that!"

Here it comes! You can feel the hair on the back of your neck standing up!

Joab pounds the podium, his voice growing bolder. "Our president was killed because he learned a horrifying truth about our government—indeed, about ALL governments—one he planned to reveal to the American people!"

His hands begin trembling wildly, his eyes bulging, as his voice grows higher and frighteningly loud. "Hiding behind the facade of human skins, the leaders of many of the most powerful nations on this Earth are actually REPTILIAN ALIENS FROM THE ALPHA DRACONIS STAR SYSTEM!"

The assembled crowd of journalists and reporters erupt into a sudden cacophony of laughter and protests!

"*Noooo!*" you cry in shock from beside the stage. "Agent Joab, what are you *doing*?! Tell them about the police reports! The target practice! The conspirators!"

But he ignores you and continues, even more unhinged.

"Kennedy *kneeeeeeeew!* He KNEW that Castro, Khrushchev, and even Queen Elizabeth herself are secret REPTILOIDS! Manipulating history! Enslaving us! So they KILLED HIM!" he rants, pulling his hands to his mouth, "They're snake people! Blood drinkers! With lizard eyes and FANGS! *FAAAAAAANGS!*" His fingers now point down in an absurd approximation of giant teeth. He's lost his mind!

The crowd bursts into even louder laughter and boos.

"Get that nut off the stage!" a voice cries from the back of the room.

The press conference has become a total disaster! Cameras flash and pens fly, capturing every word of Joab's lunatic rant to paper. Jenni Mudd shoots you a friendly smile and a wink—delighting in your abject defeat!

Agent Joab starts foaming at the mouth. Now he's howling like a wolf! He's dragged off in cuffs by security men, raving like a complete lunatic! What began so well has been brought to complete ruin!

You stand stageside in dazed shock as the mass of reporters filters out of the room. When it's nearly empty, Jenni ambles over and puts a hand on your shoulder, giving you a gentle squeeze. She chirps, "Thanks for the invite!"

Go on to the next page.

The next day, *The Dallas Morning News* reports the incident in a sea of assassination stories that pin the blame exclusively on Lee Harvey Oswald. The headline reads, *"Local Kooks Blame 'Reptilian Shapeshifters' for Kennedy's Death."* Agent Joab's terrifying bug-eyed rant becomes the face of conspiracy kooks everywhere, and brings anyone who would dare question the "Oswald as lone gunman" narrative into instant intellectual disrepute.

You realize the truth only too late. *Agent Joab never left the Agency.* He just changed jobs. He's in the Disinformation Department now—a Trojan Horse used to cover up the crimes he formerly committed by destroying the credibility of those who question the official story. [173]

And from the looks of it, he's pretty damn good at it.

YOU LOSE

Name cus ut quatue rerum alepidi freum exersqui cum reped quiaxsum fugio dolorosa ut consequunt et dolorion quitessi onnnninei conseque perio. Nequar vient nes est, occum quae. Iusti fugiasit, sunt qui quidi cus, culla aous volorepudi cus, od quiasit, si quatia corrupta doluptis saruscris es iuuestiam que faci iosum lam qui consed quos esenis cisti corqodi ulaborron tempore corio. Nem fugit ut dipeiqsa volut venis dolor qui idore odis aos quiandus di sequo et necepta quoiae giti ideraped alqu volupta buispel aos molupiatura illese musiva non pelici repiorið otur aliatsqe qiaetibus consequis sae Pudi volupta bua estur ioceitbuus volupia erpore aut labor si orrum corrune serras cum, ut et as doluptur. omnis net fic cuneri da faciassunt, volupti inunctiuri abvoicunto volorum ia lab iuru quisi voluptam fuga.

Local Kooks Blame "Reptilian Shapeshifters" For Kennedy's Death

Exclusive Photo by Jenni Mudd

Former Spy Says Aliens From Alpha Draconis Manipulate History, Drink Blood

Name cus ut quatue rerum alepidi freum exersqui cum reped quiaxsum fugio dolorosa ut consequunt et dolorion quitessi onnnninei conseque perio. Nequar vient nes est, occum quae. Iusti fugiasit, sunt qui quidi cus, culla aous volorepudi cus, od quiasit, si quatia corrupta doluptis saruscris es iuuestiam que faci iosum lam qui consed quos esenis cisti corqodi ulaborron tempore corio. Nem fugit ut dipeiqsa volut venis dolor qui idore odis aos quiandus di sequo et necepta quoiae giti ideraped alqu volupta buispel aos molupiatura illese musiva non pelici repiorið otur aliatsqe qiaetibus consequis sae Pudi volupta bua estur ioceitbuus volupia erpore aut labor si orrum corrune serras cum, ut et as doluptur. omnis net fic cuneri da faciassunt, volupti inunctiuri abvoicunto volorum ia lab iuru quisi voluptam fuga. Nam est ta, cum laccae soiste sum aut quos dlae espidorum repelum voluptio bla prorci omnis cisti omitat, il fis sent, ut laborrere pejeris am josse sum omnini nist as sut quaero labor tria corrum vendaci da, soleistia dolupta iustiam quam aui occales et ducipit iplcide seque parro earum quidquampqu serdina vitilit quam occalorro que ips psecumt? Quiat tus, nis mavli occaliorro qui at offactur cus. Est euero escoul

"Agent Joab," you reply, "I'd hate to see our chance to crack this case open be spoiled by any skeletons you have in the closet. Maybe it's better if I lead the proceedings?"

Joab nods respectfully, then replies, "Then it's settled. Tomorrow, we'll start to expose the *real* truth."

Dr. Vivalzi lets out a delighted whoop, then gives you a congratulatory peck on the cheek, saying, "Break a leg!"

That afternoon, Vivalzi works the phones, calling every reporter in the Dallas-Fort Worth metroplex, excitedly telling them, "Tomorrow morning at 9:00, The Altair Society will break news of incredible developments in the assassination investigation!"

You even take a moment to call your rival, Jenni Mudd. Her mother answers the phone and informs you she's in Dealey Plaza, investigating the assassination herself. You reply, "Tell her not to bother. Tomorrow morning, I'm cracking the case wide open!"

The next morning, it's showtime!

You arrive at the conference, wearing your best turtleneck, your hair feathered to perfection. Dozens of reporters have arrived and bark out questions at you. Jenni Mudd sits on the front row, looking strangely smug. But you'll knock that know-it-all smile off her face soon enough!

You walk to the podium, raising your hands for silence.

"Gentlemen, as the son of the Chief of Police of Dallas, I've grown up around policework, investigations, and solving difficult crimes," you begin, then chuckle, "I guess you could say—*it's in my blood.*"

Your eyes drift briefly to Jenni. She smiles innocently back, as she hands a folder to the man next to her. Strange!

But you continue, undeterred, "When I heard the news that President Kennedy had been shot, I *knew* I had to do whatever I could to help my dad solve the crime. But the shooting of a president is a far cry from *The Case of the Slippery Salamander.* And I knew if I was going to investigate it, it might call for some *unorthodox* methods."

You shoot a look at Jenni, then add, "And when I saw signs that key evidence was being stolen *right from under our noses by the FBI*, I knew I had no choice but to act!"

Go on to the next page.

Many in the crowd gasp in surprise—but the man next to Jenni stares in disgusted shock at a photo he pulled from Jenni's folder. Then his eyes drift up to you, full of murderous intent. *Why?*

Your eyes dart back to Jenni, yet she responds with only a sweet smile and a wink, as she passes the folder down the row. One by one, the men pull a photo from the folder, and pass it down, their faces all morphing from curiosity to mixes of confusion, disgust, and even hatred.

Anxiety begins to grip you as you continue, "Uh, where was I? Oh yeah. Um. So, when I saw that evidence was being stolen, I knew I had to do something, even if it meant being, well, a little unorthodox!"

"Unorthodox is right, you litle pickle smoker!" someone shouts from the crowd.

Pickle smoker? Who would try to smoke a pickle? They're wet—they'd never light!

"Queer!" someone yells from the gallery.

What's happening? Whatever Jenni's been passing around the room is turning the whole crowd against you! And you haven't even told them about the police reports of target practice in Dealey Plaza yet!

Desperate to regain control, you raise your voice, "Please, please! Let me finish! I've discovered evidence about the Kennedy assassination that points to conspiracy!"

"Shut up!" someone calls from the back of the room, "Get that turdburglar outta here!"

'Turdburglar?' What does that even mean? Your keen detective mind races to break down the etymology. *'Turd: a piece of excrement.' 'Burglar: one who breaks into someone else's...'*

Oh, no! They think you're a homosexual! *But why?*

Jenni sees your abject confusion, then lifts up the photo in her lap. It's a picture of you, examining the entrance wound on Billy's buttock out by the Packard place! She must've taken it in hiding! Now she's using it to smear you!

"Wait, no!" you cry out, "You don't understand! That picture! I was examining an entrance wound!"

The crowd bursts into laughter, and one man shouts in reply, "That you gave him, ya rump ranger!"

The crowd explodes with laughter and boos! You've lost complete control of the press conference! Everyone begins dispersing, uninterested in hearing what you've discovered!

In less than a minute, the room is empty, save for one reporter, a gentlemen with a goatee and a bright, friendly smile. He approaches you, and shakes your hand.

"Are you a reporter?" you ask weakly, "Do you want to hear what we've learned?"

He shakes his head, handing you a business card.

He replies, "I'm just in the art department at the paper. My name is Sal. *Call me.*"

Just then, two policemen storm the room and quickly cuff you. One of them recognizes you, and shakes his head sadly, saying, "So the chief's own son is a pillow biter, huh?"

The other cop replies, "That haircut. What a giveaway."

They read you your rights as they arrest you. For evidence tampering and crimes against nature.

•

The next day, *The Dallas Morning News* reports the incident in a sea of assassination stories that pin the blame exclusively on Lee Harvey Oswald. The headline reads, *"Local Deviant 'Completely Obsessed' with Kennedy Assassination, Rumps."* A photo of your utterly bewildered face, no doubt taken by Jenni during the conference, accompanies the story.

Drat! Jenni's completely destroyed you! You knew her dad worked for the FBI—but now you realize she did, too! You never should've invited her. If only you'd let Agent Joab speak, this could've turned out so differently!

YOU LOSE

ented Room Under
ked Aid to Re-
he United States
Local Deviant "Completely Obsessed" with Kennedy Assassination, Rumps
Exclusive Photo by JENNI MUDD
Perverted Policeman's Son Arrested Today for Evidence Tampering and Crimes Against Nature
Act
To Ci
ROOM
NT
DALLAS
POLICE

You decide to investigate the Mafia connection. It's a long shot, but then again, so was your crack case against Slugs O'Toole in *The Mystery of The Atomic Wedgie!*

"All right, Angelo, I'll look into this David Ferrie character," you reply. "But first, I need to call my dad and let him know I'm leaving town."

You use the Altair Society's sole phone to call your dad.

"Hey, Dad," you say when he answers, "it's me."

"Who?" he replies, confused.

"Me," you answer, annoyed, "your child."

After a moment of silence, he asks hesitantly, "Katie?"

Ugh! What a nimrod!

"It's your *son*, Dad!" you say in exasperation. "Listen, I'm going to Houston to investigate a lead. It's a long shot, but my sources say this guy knew Oswald, and may have even framed him for the shooting. His name is David Ferrie."

"Ferrie?" he replies. "Is this about the library card?"

"Library card?" you ask. "*What* library card, Dad?"

"The ... one we found ... in the wallet?" he answers hesitantly. "Of the guy what shot the ... President?"

YOWSERS! You gasp, "Wait! You found a library card for David Ferrie in Lee Harvey Oswald's *wallet*, Dad?"

But before he can answer, the phone goes dead! Then you realize: Dr. Vivalzi just hung it up!

"You can't tell him about this!" she says fearfully. "Half the police force is mobbed up! They'll give Ferrie the drop!"

Wow! It sounds like maybe Angelo's lead was hotter than you knew! David Ferrie and Oswald clearly still know each other—and perhaps intimately. You wouldn't trust just *anyone* with your library card, right? They might check out books without returning them on time—or *worse!*

Go on to the next page.

You turn to Angelo, now excited. "It sounds like we may be on to something, Angelo! I'm ready to go after him!"

"This is madness!" Professor Coppens moans.

Dr. Vivalzi agrees, saying, "Angelo, he's just a boy—"

"I may be just a boy," you reply confidently, "but I know a thing or two about solving crimes. I can do this!"

Angelo claps your shoulder, "Attaboy, kid! But listen—David Ferrie's no daisy. He's a cold-blooded psychopath. If I were you, I'd go in disguise, wearing a wire. We just need his confession on tape, not a citizen's arrest, and—"

Dr. Vivalzi jumps up in protest. "No, Angelo! It's too dangerous!" Then she turns to Joab. "Send him with a spy kit, Joab—let him try to bug Ferrie from a safe distance!"

Agent Joab brings a hand to his chin. He looks almost wistful. Then he looks at you and says, "It's your choice, Detective. I wasn't much older than you when I donned my first disguise. It can be exciting—but make no mistake, you'll be putting yourself in real danger. If you'd rather not risk it, well, I've got a trunk full of spy gear. It'd be nice for it to get used on a noble mission for a change."

Everyone turns to you, awaiting your answer. What a dilemma! You've never donned a disguise to solve a mystery before, but then again, you've never investigated a murder, unless you count *The Case of the Exsanguinated Hamster!* Something tells you that if Ferrie gets the drop on you, you'll have worse things than atomic wedgies to worry about. Maybe you should play it safer, and go as a spy instead?

If you decide to visit David Ferrie in disguise, turn to page 144.

If you decide to try to spy on him, turn to page 145.

You page the nurse repeatedly, but get no answer. You roll your wheelchair out into the halls of the nursing home. It's been deserted.

Wait! At the end of the hall there's a man hobbling along in panic on his walker. He sees you, and in terror, confirms your worst fears, crying out, "The army—they're coming! They're rounding everyone up for the FEMA camps! Run!"

"I can't walk!" you cry. "I need help! Where are the nurses?!"

"They're gone! The nurses, the doctors! They've fled north, to Canada! And they've stolen every—aiiiiiggh!"

Suddenly, he grips his chest—he's having a heart attack! He falls to the ground like a sack of potatoes.

In the distance, you hear a growing rumble, and the clear sounds of gunfire and screams. You feel the panic building within you, squeezing you like an invisible vise! *How can this be happening? This is America!* Since when does the military have the right to suspend the Constitution and depose an elected President?

Since '63, whispers the conscience you've ignored for decades, *when you helped cover up the Kennedy asssassination. For the good of the country.*

You wheel yourself quickly around the nursing home, to the cafeteria, the supply closets, the nurses stations. The man was right—they've taken everything that wasn't nailed down! There's no food left, no medicine. And then it hits you like a bomb. *They've even stolen all the toilet paper!*

And just then, your bowels surrender their booty. As does your booty.

YOU LOSE

You run as fast as you can, and duck behind the rock just in time. It looks like they didn't notice you! You can hear them talking to each other as they stroll past the door.

"How was your date with Margie?" asks the first guard, in a low, raspy voice.

"Oh, what a night!" the second guard responds. "She was all I dreamed she'd be. What a gal! And so affordable!"

They continue walking together, until they reach the big hangar door you were only moments ago about to enter. And there they stop, assuming their guard duties.

Drat! Now you'll never get in!

You decide you've had enough of Area 51. However intrigued you are by the Dallas maps and conspicuous conversation you'd recently overheard, you decide it's not worth getting shot and fined over it.

You have no choice but to sneak back into the Nevada desert, and hope for the best.

As Hangar 13 grows ever more distant behind you, you grow frustrated that you hadn't chosen to go in the door when you had the chance. What were you thinking? You'd come all this way—then chickened out at the last minute!

You're so caught up in your thoughts that you miss the small jut of metal sticking out of the sand before you. You stub your toe on it—*ouch*!

You look down and see a bright metal hatch, partially covered by tumbleweeds and ash tree branches. How strange! The hatch itself is unmarked, save for a series of numbers stamped into it: 4, 8, 15, 16, 23 and 42. What might they mean? Is it some secret code?

You peer into the small window at the hatch's center, wondering if perhaps this might be a secret entrance, a second chance at getting into Hangar 13. You begin to dig away the sand, so you can try to pull open the door. But as you clear the last bit of it away, you hear a terrifying growl coming up behind you! RIGHT BEHIND YOU!

Turn to page 140.

After a fitful night's sleep, you awaken Sunday morning, anxious and eager to return to the police station. Over breakfast, you attempt to engage your father in another conversation about the threats made to Oswald's life.

"Dad," you begin, "I really think Oswald might need extra protection today. Half the country wants him dead, and he's just so important to cracking this case that—"

"Honey!" he calls out to your mom in the kitchen. "More pancakes, baby! And, and, more of that stuff you put on 'em, makes 'em so yummy! The uh, uh, that sugary brown stuff? What pours out of the, uh, spout thing ...?"

"*Syrup*, Dad," you mutter, defeated, "it's called syrup." It's hopeless. His mind, if he has one, is made up.

He drives you back to the station, his Ford radio blaring as he tunelessly sings along with Peter, Paul and Mary.

*"How many deaths will it take 'til he knows
that too many people have died?
The answer, my friend, is blowin' in the wind ..."*

Back inside the station, you find your way to the basement, where Oswald is just being cuffed to his escort, the genial detective Jim Leavelle. Jim smiles at you pleasantly.

"Hey, Detective," he drawls, tipping his trademark light tan cowboy hat to you. "What brings ya up here?"

"My dad said I could tag along, I hope you don't mind."

"Well, 'spose if your dad says it's all right," he shrugs, turning to Oswald. "Lee, if anybody shoots at you, I hope they're as good a shot as you are."

Oswald chuckles good-naturedly, then replies, "Well, nobody is going to shoot at me."

With his rejoinder hanging in the air, the procession begins. Jim leads the way through the basement corridors, Oswald trudging along on his left side, you on his right.

Go on to the next page.

As you push open the door to the garage, you're amazed at the flood of reporters and police. There must be a hundred people crowded in there! You scan the crowd for any possible signs of threat—yet every face seems the same as the rest, no obvious crackpots or lunatics amongst them.

A horn honks. You flinch in overreaction, your heart pounding loudly in your chest.

It was just a horn, you tell yourself. *Nothing more.*

Oswald's transfer car awaits, the door open, no more than thirty feet ahead of you. The crowds have parted like the Red Sea before Moses to allow the suspect and his escort through. Two dozen cameras are trained on the three of you—history being made in this very moment—broadcast to TV sets all over the world. It only just now hits you that you yourself are becoming a part of American history, simply by being there, the gangly boy in the turtleneck, walking alongside the tan-suited detective and the presumed assassin of the 35th President of the United States of America. How strange a thought that seems!

Twenty feet to the car. Now fifteen. You're going to make it! Your fears were misplaced.

And then it happens.

A thick, pug-like man in a grey fedora leaps out from the crowd, a snubnosed .38 aimed squarely at Oswald's gut. Time slows to a crawl, and without thinking, you leap in front of Oswald, pushing him back, your hands in a defensive posture, screaming at the armed man, *"Don't shoot!"*

But it's too late. He's already pulling the trigger.

BANG!

Yet he's missed his target! The bullet meant to kill Oswald doesn't hit him. Detective Leavelle jerks Oswald back and covers him heroically with his body, as other cops tackle the shooter and pin him to the ground, disarmed.

It's only just then, as the cameras flash and reporters and cops surround you, that you realize who was shot.

Turn to page 134.

The pain in your chest is agonizing! In and out of consciousness you fade, catching only glimpses of the minutes after. Faces leaning over you in the ambulance. The blaring sirens. You cling desperately to life, as it dances near you, then away, then back again. The flood of lights in the emergency room. Doctors working frantically to stanch the bleeding. Cold towels pressed to your head.

A priest, giving you the last rites.

"No no no... " you groan in quiet agony. "Please no."

Then suddenly, your mother's sweet, caring face leans over your own, tears pouring down her cheeks. How did she get here so fast? Is that a halo over her head? She holds your face in her hands.

"Are you ... an angel?" you whisper.

"No, no, son, it's me," she whispers back gently, kissing your cheek. But she's fading—the light all around her is disappearing.

"What happened, Mom?" you manage to ask.

You hear her voice from a faraway place whispering back, "They tried to silence Oswald. But you ..." She starts to choke up. "You stopped them, you brave, foolish boy."

"Whoooo?" you hear someone ask. *Did I really stop them?* You try to look around, but you can't find the strength. Your eyes are too heavy to hold open any longer. You close them. But her sweet voice remains—at least for the moment.

"Oswald is talking, son. He wasn't the shooter. He's an intelligence agent. And he's naaaming naaaaaaaaames." Her voice is slowing, growing ever fainter.

"Youuu wooon't belieeeeeve hooooowww hiiiiiigh uuuuuup iiiit goooooooooooeees ..."

You feel like you're floating away. You can see your pale, white body on the operating table, the gaping wound on your chest. Your eyes are closed, a sad smile on your pale face. You can see your mother whispering into your ear, as doctors and nurses desperately try to save you. She's telling you who really killed Kennedy. But you can't hear her anymore. Because you're dead.

YOU LOSE

136

You decide to trust your father's instincts for some completely idiotic and inexplicable reason.

Seriousy, we've already established that your father is a jabbering idiot who can barely construct a coherent sentence. We've also already demonstrated that *you* are a preternaturally gifted kid detective with an incredible sense of intuition and considerable deductive reasoning skills.

Furthermore, even if the *real* you is irredeemably stupid and uninformed, you have to at *least* know enough about American history to know that Oswald was shot during his basement transfer. You'd even seen *proof* of death threats!

And yet you *still* chose to trust your dad's instincts and not offer Oswald any additional protection at all! This author can only assume that means you are so utterly and completely spineless that the even prospects of simply *reading* about your inevitable fictive demise heroically protecting the doomed Oswald would just be too much for your tender sensibilities to endure.

Which means, of course, that you, dear reader, are even worse than an idiot. You are a complete wuss. And when you put down the book in frustration only moments from now, you'll still be a wuss. And your wussdom will haunt you for the rest of your wussy days.

Wuss.

YOU LOSE

Or, if you attempt to overcome your obvious wussdom by impotently confronting your father over dinner the following night, turn to page 152.

138

After a few days, you reluctantly decide to call Jenni up and ask what her investigation unearthed.

To your surprise, her father, the FBI agent, answers the call. When he hears it's you on the line, he erupts in hearty laughter, then calls out, "Jennifer, call for you."

In the distance, you hear her ask, "Who is it, Dad?"

"Betsy Wetsy!" he says, with an even heartier laugh.

After a few seconds, she picks up the phone.

"Hey, Turtleneck," she says. "Sorry about that."

You try to sound casual, ignoring the slight, and ask, "So, my mom took me off the case. But you're still on it, right? Have you learned anything? I'm dying to know."

"Actually," she replies, "my dad took me off it, too. Said it was pretty open and shut. Oswald did it. Alone."

You want to argue—about the rigged lineup, the prior contact between Oswald and FBI Agent Hosty—but you know it's hopeless. You appeal to her ego, instead.

"But what about your book deal?" you ask. "With your keen detective mind, I figured you'd crack this wide open, and become America's most famous child sleuth."

She laughs, then says, "Funny you should mention it. I still have the book deal. I pitched them on a series, though. A clever schoolgirl detective. Her wisecracking FBI dad. With all the cases I've solved, I figured, the books would just write themselves, right? I'll send you a copy, Turtleneck."

Go on to the next page.

A few months later, you get a copy in the mail. As does everyone in your class at school. As if that wasn't bad enough, her *Annie Grimes* series becomes a blockbuster hit, too—selling millions of copies to kids across America and earning Jenni fortune and fame. *Ugh!*

But it earns you a little something, too. Thanks to her immortalization of your botched puppy frame-up job in her debut book *Annie Grimes and the Case of the Framed Chihuahua*, you become almost as famous as Jenni Mudd and her thinly-veiled proxy, Annie Grimes. For she's incorporated a thinly veiled proxy of YOU into the books—as the hapless, bumbling, would-be rival to Annie Grimes. The son of an incompetent Chief of Police, a boy both incompetent AND incontinent.

For the rest of your life, your friends no longer call you "Turtleneck." They call you "Betsy Wetsy."

And you live a long, long time.

YOU LOSE

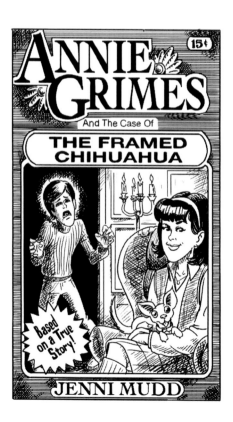

You turn around quickly—and are shocked at the sight! A gigantic polar bear is racing through the desert towards you with the speed of a freight train!

Your keen detective's mind floods with questions as the bear closes in!

How did a polar bear end up in the middle of the desert?!

The bear is almost on you!

What is in the hatch?!

It's rearing up on its hind legs!

What do the numbers signify?!

It's raising its enormous paws to strike!

How does this tie in to the bigger mysteries you've uncovered?

The bear swipes with the speed and fury of a hurricane, taking your detective's mind right off of things. Or, put another away, taking your head right off your shoulders!

As your now decapitated head rolls to a stop twenty feet away, you find yourself staring at a little ant wandering happily along the desert floor. Only it's no longer happy—because you've landed right on an antpile! An army of angry ants come flooding out—and they're heading straight up your lolling tongue, biting every inch of it! ARGH!

As your brain slowly begins to starve for oxygen, you can't help but feel a little cheated by this absurdly arbitrary and randomly cruel turn of events. What a gigantic waste of your time—and your life!

46 years later, millions of Americans will share in your pain. Except, you know, for the decapitation part.

YOU LOSE

You stumble into the hangar, fully expecting to see a flying saucer. But instead, you see a figure in a spacesuit. He's attached to wires, being lifted in the air as he bounds around a barren landscape of powder and rock.

Slowly, it dawns on you ... It's some kind of fake lunar surface! Area 51 isn't hiding aliens and spaceships, it's a gigantic movie set! NASA's rehearsing for a fake moon landing! Is that why Kennedy died? Because he asked NASA to do the impossible–putting a man on the moon in less than a decade?

Suddenly, the "astronaut" produces a gun!

Oh, no!

A million more questions flood through your brain! Followed by a bullet.

YOU LOSE

144

"All right," you reply. "I'll go in disguise. But as who?"

Angelo breaks into a huge smile, laughing. "Why, as a Mafia delivery boy, of course!"

"A delivery boy?" you ask in shock. "Delivering what?"

He picks up the files you filched from Evidence Control, "Police reports of shooters engaged in target practice in Dealey Plaza. Trust you me, Ferrie's gonna want these!"

Joab's eyes light up. "I've got to admit, Angelo—that's brilliant. While you and Vivalzi get him in disguise, I'll take photos of these reports for Altair records. I still think this assassination has CIA fingerprints all over it, but Ferrie, well, he's in bed with the Mob, the CIA, and worse. And a Mafia delivery boy with incriminating reports may be just the key we need to get him to talk."

An hour later, with your hair dyed black, a Grundig TK40 tape deck taped to your stomach, and a Mafia delivery-boy outfit that looks as Italian as spaghetti and meatballs, you're ready to board a bus to Houston and crack this case wide open!

Angelo sizes you up with a smile, "Well, you sure *look* like a Mafia delivery boy. But how's your Italian accent?"

Without skipping a beat, you begin gesticulating wildly with your hands as you half-shout, "My name-ah is-ah Mario! *Now-ah that's-ah spicy meat-ah-ball-ah!*"

"That's super, Mario," he says, "My own mother would think you were from the old country. Let's get you on a bus!"

Turn to page 146.

"I think Vivalzi's right," you answer. "I think I'd rather play it safe and try to spy on Ferrie."

Angelo seems disappointed, but shrugs. "Fair enough, kid. Joab, let's get him his gear and get him on the road."

Agent Joab leads you to the Altair Society's storage room, and opens up an old, battered Army trunk. Inside it, you see a dozen curious spy gadgets and gizmos. *Zowie!*

He notes your interest. "This cigarette lighter? A tiny camera. This umbrella? A poison dart gun. Pencil bombs. Exploding cigars. All too dangerous for a kid, of course."

Your eyes train on a shiny silver dollar with a strange dent near its bottom. He takes it out, and flips it in the air.

"And this?" he says with a haunted smile. "This is—or was—my suicide coin. If I was caught behind enemy lines?"

He squeezes the coin face between finger and thumb, and *boing!* A tiny needle pops out of the bottom.

"It used to contain saxitoxin," he explains, "a thousand times deadlier than sarin. One tiny poke, I'd be dead in seconds. But it's disarmed. Now it's just my lucky coin."

He squeezes the coin again, and the needle disappears.

Agent Joab looks at it pensively, contemplating something. Then he places it in your hands.

"Here," he says warmly, "I want you to have it. See this dent here? This coin stopped a KGB bullet that was aimed right for my heart. It's brought me good luck ever since."

"It's an honor, Agent Joab," you say, tucking the coin in your pants pocket, "I hope it brings me luck, too."

Turn to page 149.

It's a dark and stormy night, and the bus ride to Houston seems to take forever. The prospect of going undercover to penetrate the Mob has you trembling with excitement—or is it terror? Clever disguises, false identities and hidden tape decks are tools that BIG TIME detectives use every day— and now, it looks like you're one of them!

Eat that, Jenni Mudd! you muse to yourself.

To help pass the time, you slip into the bathroom of the giant Scenicruiser bus to record a few mic tests with the painfully heavy tape deck hidden under your shirt.

"A-hello-ah!" you say, speaking towards your chest. "My name-ah is-a Mario! And I'm-a gonna stomp-ah you goombahs and a-solve-ah this-a murder-ah! *Here we gooo!*"

You play it back. It's crystal clear! But the Grundig weighs thirty pounds, and the batteries burn hot when you're using it. So you decide to give it a rest, return to your seat and devise a plan for fooling David Ferrie into a confession.

Go on to the next page.

Sometime after midnight, with the storm still raging, the bus pulls into the beautiful art deco Greyhound bus depot in Houston. You sprint through heavy sheets of rain towards the entrance. Lightning bolts flash, freezing a million drops of water around you in midair. You get soaked! Luckily, a cab waits under the covered cab stand.

The grizzled cabbie barely glances at you in the mirror, drawling in bored annoyance, "So where we goin'?"

"To-ah the Alamont-ah hotel-ah," you reply, "And step-ah on it-ah! I gotta hot-ah delivery-ah for-ah a wiseguy-ah! And he don't like-ah to be kep-ah-ta waiting-ah, *capisce?*"

He *capisces,* all right! In a matter of seconds, his taxi is flying at the speed of sound through the torrential Houston rains. You're there in minutes. You leap out of the car and race once again through the rain, this time into the warm, dry respite of the Alamont Hotel lobby.

A dark-haired beauty at the front desk smiles as you enter, "Wow—you really got soaked out there, sir!"

"Mamma mia!" you reply, in your utterly authentic Italian accent. "It'sa tempest-ah outta there-ah!"

She hands you a clean towel from behind the desk, then asks brightly, "Do you have a reservation, sir?"

"Ah, no-ah!" you reply, totally cool. "I have-ah a special delivery-ah, for a mister-ah David Ferrie-ah."

She checks her reservation book, then frowns. "I'm sorry—it looks like Mr. Ferrie hasn't arrived yet. Would you like to wait for him here in the lobby?"

Then she smiles, tucking a loose strand of her thick, black Italian hair behind her ear. "Or you could wait with me in the bar? I'm going on break—I'd love some company."

Wow—she's really cute! And even a thickie like your dad could figure out she's flirting with you! But what to do? You have time to kill—why not pass it with a beautiful girl?

If you decide to join her in the bar, turn to page 154.

If you wait for David Ferrie in the lobby, turn to page 148.

You reply, "I'm-a so sorry-ah, some other time-ah, eh?" She sighs, disappointed, and heads off to the bar alone.

You plant yourself on a long, blue twill couch in the lobby, your eyes watching the hotel entrance like a hawk. The storm rages unabated outside, thunderbolts booming from nearby lightning strikes every minute or two. Occasionally, suspicious-looking figures in shiny pinstripes push through the revolving door. But hours pass, and still no sign of Ferrie.

Turn to page 155.

Joab then pulls a hefty Grundig TK40 tape deck from the trunk, placing it and a few peripherals into a briefcase.

"This little guy," he says, holding up a shiny disc, "is your phone bug. Screw off a mouthpiece, drop it in, it broadcasts to a receiver on the deck. Very easy to use—but it's an older model. The broadcast range is only about 50 feet. So try to get a room near Ferrie's. The closer, the better."

Then, as if remembering something, he grabs a brushed metal capsule. He pulls it open, revealing a lockpit kit.

"Know how to use one of these, Detective?" he asks.

You smile. "I sure do—I had to learn how to solve *The Case of the Locker-Trapped Nerd* last year."

His eyes growing wistful again, he says, "This little baby got me out of a lot of jams. Every undercover spy needs a rectal lockpit kit like this. Don't worry. It's clean."

He places it in the briefcase and hands it to you. You feel a tingle of excitement! You started the day as a carefree kid, but you'll be ending it as a bona fide American spy chasing Mafia bad guys in the biggest murder case in American history. Not bad!

(You know, except for the unspeakable tragedy part.)

Turn to page 150.

It's a dark and stormy night, and the bus ride to Houston seems to take forever. The prospect of a spy mission to surveil a psychotic Mafia lackey with ties to an assassination has you trembling with excitement—or is it terror?

On the long drive down, you test your recorder. It works like a charm! You'll just need to figure out which room he's in, and set up somewhere close enough to monitor him.

After midnight, with the storm still raging, the bus pulls into the Houston depot. You dash through heavy sheets of rain towards the entrance. Lightning bolts flash, freezing a million drops of water around you in midair. You get soaked! Luckily, a cab waits under the covered cab stand.

The grizzled cabbie barely glances at you in the mirror, drawling in bored annoyance, "So where we goin'?"

"Alamont Hotel," you answer.

He starts driving, apparently on the scenic route to run up the fare. But at least you're drier when you arrive!

Go on to the next page.

A dark-haired beauty at the front desk looks surprised at the sight of you. "Um, can I help you?"

You'll need a room next to Ferrie's—but you don't know which one he's in. Your keen instincts devise a distraction!

"I need a room for the night," you reply, "and you should have a delivery for me, too. Last name 'Curry?'"

She's caught off guard, and begins looking under the counter for a delivery that won't be found. While she's distracted, you lean over the desk to peek at the reservation book. There it is. David Ferrie, Room 228. He's not checked in yet. And conveniently, it looks like Room 227 is free!

"I don't see anything," she says, "You sure it arrived?"

"I sure hope so," you reply, worried, "It's medication—I'll need it by tomorrow. Oh well. I'll need a room for tonight. Any chance you've got 227 available? It's my birthday—I'm a bit superstitious like that."

She checks her book, "Yes, it looks like 227 is free."

"Great," you reply, "Room for one please."

Five minutes later, you're in Room 227! It's a drab affair—water stains on the ceiling, lumpy bed, and a musty odor in the air. You drop the briefcase on the bed, pop it open, and take out the phone bug and rectal lockpit kit.

Then you open the door and peer out into the hall, looking furtively in both directions. With the coast clear, you set to work on the lock of Room 228. You insert the tension wench, then use a thin pick to try to count the pins. Five of them. One by one, you work them up to a soft click. After a couple of minutes, you've flipped four. You're almost there! But suddenly, you hear the clear *DING!* of the elevator chime at the end of the hall! Oh no—someone's coming!

If you try to pop the last lock pin, turn to page 156.

If you dash back into your room, turn to page 158.

With Oswald dead, any hopes of a trial are forever lost. Though you chose the path of total wussdom, you summon the courage to at least confront your father for his part in this travesty when he gets home that night for dinner.

"Honey?" he calls as he steps in the door. "You wouldn't *believe* the day I had! I'm starved. What's for dinner?"

"What's for dinner?!" you yell. "How about hot plate of crow, Dad, with a side of humble pie!?"

His eyes widen curiously. "Well, I never had crow before, son, but if your mom's cooking it, I'm game to—"

"I'M cooking it, Dad!" you boom in an impotent rage. "It's an IDIOM! Sounds like IDIOT! Looks like YOU!"

He looks stunned, like you're speaking in tongues.

"The death threats, Dad?" you scream. "The calls last night? Alveeta's note? I TOLD you his life was in danger!"

Your father reaches into his pocket. "Alveeta's note? You mean this? The one she found in the trash last night?"

He hands you a crumpled up piece of paper.

You put aside your white-hot rage long enough to uncrumple it. It's a phone log record from the switchboard operator's pool. Evidence Oswald tried to make a call last night—to someone named John Hurt in Raleigh.

"What a minute!" you say. "Oswald tried to call someone last night? Who, Dad? WHO?!"

He shrugs. "I dunno. Louise Swinney was on duty then. Oswald wanted to call somebody, but those guys what protect the President wouldn't let her place it. Alveeta found the note in the trash." 172

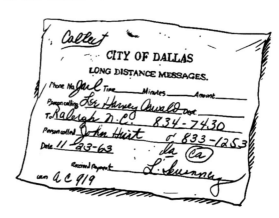

Go on to the next page.

"*The Secret Service?*" you ask, your keen detective mind flooding with new questions. "They stopped an outgoing call from the assassin? Who is this Hurt guy, Dad?"

Your father shrugs stupidly and starts towards the kitchen. "Does it really matter now, son? Oswald's dead—and *I'm* starved. Let's eat some crow!"

•

That night, after an awkward dinner, you call Jenni Mudd, the note in hand. She just might be able to help.

"Hey, Turtleneck," she chirps, "Looks like your dad strikes again. *The Case of the Botched Protection Job.*"

"Jenni," you interrupt, "I know. He's an idiot. Listen, I've got new evidence here, a phone number. Oswald tried to place a call last night, but the Secret Service wouldn't let the operator put it through. Can you look the number up?"

Jenni whistles in surprise. "Wow! Intriguing! Maybe a fellow conspirator, huh? What's the number?"

You give it to her, and she replies, "MY dad can find out anything. I'll let you know what I learn, Turtleneck."

The next morning at school, she finds you at your locker, a strangely grim look on her face.

"So, my dad looked up the number," she says quietly.

"And?" you ask, dying of curiosity.

"John D. Hurt of Raleigh, North Carolina, is in military intelligence," she says, dropping her voice to a whisper. "And my dad said to tell you to drop it. Or else."

"Or else *what?*" you bark, to the surprise of the students nearby. "He'll have me *killed*? For finding proof that Oswald was connected to the military intelligence?"

"Yep," she says, walking away.

You're about to chase after her and demand an explanation, but then remember something. You're a wuss. And in the face of true danger, you've only got one option.

And, with the world's most pathetic sigh, you shrug helplessly, then head off to history class, content just to study it, rather than risk changing it. Wuss.

YOU LOSE

If I'm going to have to wait around until Ferrie shows up, you tell yourself, *why not do it with a beautiful girl?*

You offer her a mischevious wink and reply, "You make-ah it sound-ah so good-ah! I don't-ah suppose a little drink-ah would-ah hurt-ah none-ah. Let's-ah go, *principessa!*"

She offers a devilish smile back. "Let's!"

A minute later, you're sitting on a worn, red leather barstool beside Texas' answer to Sophia Loren! She raises a manicured finger to flag the burly, olive-skinned bartender.

"Mitch," she says, "two Hurricane Carlas, pronto."

He eyes you skeptically, then says, "I'm not sure your little friend here could handle it, Francesca." He turns to you. "What say I whip you up something a little more your style? Shirley Temple, rocks?" He lets out a bullying cackle.

"Oh, Mitch, lay off." Francesca says. "I'm sure he's more than man enough for a little drink."

She turns and looks at you expectantly, placing a hand on your knee. Her blue-green eyes sparkle like the Mediterranean Sea, beckoning you to dive into them.

Zowie! What a dilemma! You've never had an alcoholic beverage in your life, and aren't sure you should start while in the middle of a super-secret spy mission. But then again, if you order the Shirley Temple, you'll look like a wimp!

If you order the Hurricane Carla, turn to page 159.

If you go with a Shirley Temple, turn to page 160.

You're beginning to nod off, exhausted from this seemingly never-ending day, when a frightening-looking fellow with huge, painted-on black eyebrows pushes fast through the revolving door. His red wig is soaked and crooked. It looks like a guinea pig died on his head!

He's followed by two handsome younger fellows, both with suitcases. They head straight to the front desk, and in less than a minute, the desk clerk is handing them a key.

You decide to tail them from a distance as they head up the stairs. By the time you're on the second floor, Ferrie and his crew are already heading into their room. You can hear the chain-lock being set from here.

You approach the door, pausing only to lift your shirt and hit the RECORD button. The batteries warm quickly—it's on! Through the door, a muffled exchange is underway.

You raise a hand and rap twice, and in five seconds, you're standing face to terrifying face with the target.

"Mr. Ferrie-ah," you reply, "I'm-a here to see you-ah."

"Who are you?!" he roars, with breath that smells like bourbon and cigarettes. "What do you want?!"

It's only now you notice he has a .38 Special tucked in the front of his pants, with his right hand resting on it!

If you chuckle warmly and tell him you're a friend, turn to page 161.

If you glare back and tell him Fanucci sent you with a special delivery, turn to page 162.

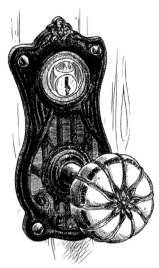

You know you're close! You give the lock a final jostle, and feel the unmistakable click of the last pin. *Bingo!*

You slip with lightning speed into Room 228, closing the door behind you. Ferrie's room is a mirror of your own, with the added touch of a cockroach near the telephone. It scrambles into hiding on your approach.

With a tight grip, you unscrew the mouthpiece of the shiny black Bakelite phone, revealing the bright red carbon granule microphone. You gently lift it, and slide the thin disc of the phone bug into the space beneath. Then you rescrew the mouthpiece, wipe it clean of any fingerprints. *It's done!*

With the first part of your mission complete, you slip back into the hall, locking the door behind you. Moments later, you've set up the Grundig on the small table near the wall you share with Room 228.

You slip on the headphones, and flip on the deck. A tiny red light indicates it's receiving a signal. Good job! Now all you have to do is hope Ferrie makes it tonight!

Hours pass, with still no sign of Ferrie. You're beginning to nod off when a loud BANG! startles you awake. A gunshot? No, a door slam. Someone's in Room 228! You press a glass to the wall to listen—but whoever is in there is being awfully quiet!

They might be going straight to sleep! warns the keen detective's voice in your mind.

You need to get something incriminating on tape! But what if Ferrie never uses the phone? You might just be missing out on the best chance anyone will *ever* get of catching him in a confession!

But then, your inner Sherlock pipes up helpfully, *Just give him a call—he'll have to answer!*

You turn on your Grundig recorder, pick up the room phone, and dial 2-2-8.

The loud ring of the phone is audible through the thin hotel wall—along with a sudden panicked expletive! You hear another argument taking place—about whether or not to answer it. Just when you're beginning to fear they won't, you hear a voice on the other end.

"Hello?!" an infuriated voice screams at you. "Who the (EXPLETIVE) is this? AND WHY ARE YOU CALLING ME AT FOUR IN THE MORNING?!"

If you yell back at him to let him know who's boss, turn to page 165.

If you whisper, "Your library card was in Oswald's wallet. If you want it back, you best listen up.", turn to page 166.

You can't risk getting caught! You leap back to your door, fumbling in your pockets for the room key. The elevator opens. A gigantic brute of a man in the shiniest green suit you've ever seen begins lumbering down the hall towards you. Is this a hitman who's come to kill you?

He stops at a door two rooms down. Another guest?

You pull out the room key and try to jam it in the lock. It doesn't fit anymore! *Wait, that's your house key!*

You reach back in your pocket, still panicking, your teeth chattering in fear as you grip the key. You pull it out and try to shove it in the lock. *Oh no, it's Joab's lucky coin!*

Your continued panicked fumbling finally gets the giant's attention. His eyes narrow and brow furls. He begins moving your way, looking like some gigantic gorilla headed to a St. Patrick's Day prom. *Your adrenaline levels skyrocket!*

This is your last chance! You reach in your pocket once more, and pull out a key with 227 stamped on it. Finally! You slip it into the lock, turn, and fly into your room. You close the door, and lock it. Then for safety's sake, you lock the door chain, too—just as he starts banging on the door!

"Hey kid!" growls the impossibly deep voice. "You left your lock pick out here! Let me give it back to you!"

BANG! BANG! Your heart is beating so fast it's about to explode! You race into the bathroom, your anxiety soaring! You hardly have time to be disgusted by the sight of the clogged toilet, full to the top with discolored water. Because suddenly, you hear the outside door get kicked open!

Then it happens. Darkness closes in on you! YOU'RE FAINTING IN FEAR! The last thing you see before you pass out is dirty toilet water racing up to break your fall. *Ugh!*

Years later, the suspicious nature of your death by drowning in a Mafia-owned hotel toilet prompts conspiracy buffs to call you "the first silenced witness in the JFK case." Luckily, you're not around to tell them it was suicide by stupidity. Maybe the coin helped, after all?

YOU LOSE

Mitch the bartender shrugs and whips up two Hurricane Carlas on the spot, serving you both a red-orange concoction in a surprisingly small glass. He garnishes yours with a pink paper umbrella in an obvious insult to your masculinity.

Eager to disabuse them both of any notions of your wimpiness, you throw back the minuscule drink as if it were a cup of milk. To your surprise, it tastes sweet and tropical, like there was hardly alcohol in it at all! Maybe there's not?

"Ahhhhh," you sigh happily, "how-ah refreshing-ah!"

And that's when Hurricane Carla hits you with the full force of the nightmarish storm that devastated the Texas coast only two years ago!

The room is spinning madly! You feel as if you just got off the world's fastest Tilt-a-Whirl! You grip the bar to hold yourself in place, only to discover you've already lost your balance and are tumbling backwards off the stool and onto the dirty red berber carpet of the hotel bar. The full weight of the Grundig smashes into your belly, causing you to scream out in agony, "Oh, my stomach!"

In your inebriated confusion, you forgot to maintain your super authentic Italian accent! The gorgeous hotel clerk is suddenly at your side on the floor—feeling the bulging spy apparatus hiding underneath your shirt.

She turns to Mitch, spitting out some unknowable command in Italian.

Then Mitch pulls out a snubnosed .38 and levels it right between your eyes, replying, "It's-ah my pleasure-ah!"

It occurs to you that maybe the reason the carpets are red is so they won't show blood. Good guess.

YOU LOSE

You remind yourself that you're on a secret mission, and the target is David Ferrie, not Italian booty.

You shrug sheepishly, then reply, "It's-ah been-ah long-ah day-ah, Francesca-ah. I think-ah I'll just have-ah a Shirley-ah Temple-ah for now-ah."

She turns to Mitch with an annoyed sigh and says, "And, Mitch, I'll have my drink over there." She points to the barstool farthest from you.

She slides her shapely body off the stool and walks with an alluring wriggle to the far away stool. Mitch the bartender chuckles, then slides you a Shirley Temple.

"Here you go, sir," he says "Shirley Temple, rocks."

You take a sip. Blech! It tastes like he made it with seltzer instead of 7-UP. But rather than draw attention to yourself by complaining, you drink it quietly, and then, with a tilt of your hat to the still annoyed Francesca, you return to the lobby to wait for the target.

You plant yourself on a long, blue twill couch in the lobby, your eyes watching the hotel entrance like a hawk. The storm rages unabated outside, thunder bolts booming from nearby lightning strikes every minute or two. Occasionally, suspicious-looking figures in shiny pinstripes push through the revolving door. But hours pass, and still no sign of Ferrie.

Turn to page 155.

"Ha, oh no-ah, you-ah misunderstand-ah," you chuckle warmly. "I'm a friend-ah, here-ah to see you-ah."

Ferrie's expression only darkens at your attempts to calm him with harmless chuckles.

"How do you know my name, *friend*?!" he growls, his hand adjusting his wig, "and what are you laughing at?"

He thinks you're laughing at his wig! the keen detective inside you warns. *Don't look at it!*

You try to calm his nerves. "Oh-ah, I'm-ah thinking you must-ah be-ah a funny-ah guy, that's all-ah. I have-ah important business to-ah discuss-ah with you-ah."

"I'm funny?" he replies, growing angrier, "Funny how? Like I'm a clown? I amuse you? I make you laugh? HOW THE FUDGE AM I FUNNY?!"

Only he didn't say "fudge." He said the F-word! He's furious! He pulls his .38 out lightning fast—and in seconds, he's shoving it in your face! You'll have to calm him down!

"No no no!" you reply as calmly as you can, "You-ah got it all-ah wrong-ah! I'm-ah no laughing at you-ah. I'm-ah here to bring-ah you something-ah, a gift, so to speak-ah."

He stares deeply into your eyes, trying to read you. And as he does, the wet, furry guinea pig pelt on his head slides completely off the side and onto the carpet. It looks so utterly absurd, sitting there on the ground like a dead rat. Despite your best efforts, a tiny laugh escapes your lungs. And with that, Ferrie makes his decision.

BANG!

On the bright side, at least you died with a smile on your face.

YOU LOSE

You put on your best Mafia tough-guy face and glare back, replying with a menacing whisper, "My name-ah is Mario. And you, Mr. Ferrie-ah, need-ah to show a little-ah more-ah respect-ah for our friend-ah Mr. Fanucci-ah."

His eyes go wide with surprise, and he pulls you into the hotel room. He turns to his two younger accomplices and tells them, "Al, Melvin—give us a minute, all right?"

Without a word, the two leave the room. It's only you and Ferrie now. He pulls the gun from his pants and lays it on a dirty tabletop nearby.

"Sorry, sorry, just a little jumpy, that's all. Crazy day," he says, taking a breath. "So what do you got for me?"

You open your briefcase and pull out the police reports.

"Special delivery-ah," you reply, "from-ah your friends in-ah the Dallas-ah Police-ah Department. I mean, Department-ah."

He takes the reports from you with lightning speed and starts reading them. But then, the suspicion returns to his face. "Why would I care about some, some kooks play-shooting in Dealey Plaza? I got nothing to do with that madness up there— they caught the guy, right? That Castro-lover? I'm down here to look at a skating rink, that's all!"

Then you drop the bomb. "Mr. Ferrie-ah. We found-ah your library card in Mr. Oswald's wallet-ah. So, I am thinking, you maybe should-ah drop-ah the pretense-ah. We are, ah, 'ow you say—on-ah the same-ah team-ah, no?"

David Ferrie's eyes go wide with panic—the color drains from his face. He's shaking with outright terror.

"No, no, no! That's—oh! Hell! Lee, you stupid son of a bitch!" he stammers, now clearly desperate. "You, you gotta help me get that card! You gotta!"

You nod sympathetically, "Yes-ah, we are-ah working on that right-ah now. We can't-ah have Mr. Oswald tied to the man-ah who was-ah only hours ago sitting beside Mr. Marcello in a courtroom-ah, no?"

David Ferrie lets out a horrified wail. His defenses are finally down—now it's time to get your confession and go!

Go on to the next page.

"Mr. Ferrie-ah, we are-ah gonna make-ah this go away," you reply gently, "but you didn't-ah make it easy-ah."

Ferrie nods, sweat pouring down his head, "I know, I know—that card! How could I be so stupid?!"

"In-ah the Old Country," you say, "when-ah we frame a patsy for a killing-ah, as you did-ah Mr. Oswald, we make-ah sure we cover our tracks-ah. Not-ah leave a road-map in his-ah pocket that leads right-ah back-ah to Mr. Marcello-ah."

Ferrie breaks into tears, "I know, I know—I thought I'd covered everything!" Then, just as fast, the anger returns. "But our guys on the force were s'posed to pop Lee in the theater!? What the hell happened there?"

Wow! They'd even planned to have mobbed-up cops kill Oswald! You're getting great stuff on tape!

"He will be-ah taken care of, soon-ah," you bluff.

"Yeah, yeah— I know," he says, "Ruby's on it."

Yikes! So the Mob's already got a hitman assigned? You'll have to call your dad and warn him Oswald is in danger! You've got all you need on tape—time to get out!

"Mr. Ferrie-ah, don't worry," you say, in the voice of an old, dear friend. "We are-ah gonna fix this-ah. Nobody is-ah gonna know-ah that Mr. Kennedy was-ah killed by-ah the Mafia. But next time, try-ah not-ah to be-ah so sloppy-ah, eh? More-ah headaches for all of us-ah— who needs it, eh?"

Ferrie closes his eyes and lets out a relieved sigh. "You're right, Mario. You're right. Next time. No mistakes."

Turn to page 164.

You turn to go. Suddenly, Ferrie races forward and embraces you in obvious gratitude! You hear a click—then the telltale sound of a tape rewinding. He recoils from you in sudden horror! Then his hands dart out to feel your stomach.

Your own voice booms loudly from your gut, "My name-ah is-a Mario! And I'ma gonna stomp-ah you goombahs and a-solve-ah this-a murder-ah! *Here we gooo!*"

Ferrie staggers back in horror— then grabs his .38! Mamma mia! Looks like it's game over for you, Mario!

YOU LOSE

You decide to fight fire with fire, screaming back, "I (EXPLETIVE)-ing work with Sergeant Fanucci in Dallas! Put David Ferrie on the (EXPLETIVE)-ing phone or there's going to be some (EXPLETIVE) (EXPLETIVE) (EXPLETIVE)!"

"What the—?" whispers the voice. Click. He hung up!

You place the glass against the wall—hoping to catch something—then wonder whether you should call him back. But you aren't wondering long. The door to your room is suddenly kicked open by David Ferrie himself—and he's got a .38 pointed right at you!

He must've heard you through the walls... your inner detective helpfully concludes. *Next time you're bugging the phone of a psychopath from the adjacent room, you probably should keep your voice down.*

But there is no next time.

YOU LOSE

With your Grundig tape deck recording every word, you gently whisper, "David Ferrie, I'm with the Dallas Police. A friend of Sergeant Fanucci."

"What? Dallas Police?" he barks back. "I don't know nobody named Fanucci. Why are you calling me? Huh?!"

"Because," you reply, "we found your library card in the wallet of the assassin of the President of the United States."

"What?! The hell you say?" he says, his panic obvious. "My library card? In the wallet of that crazy sumbitch that popped the President?! That ain't possible!"

He's still playing the fool! You'll have to press him!

"David—shut up and listen," you whisper in a menacing tone. "Your card is going to disappear, just like our police reports of shooters target practicing in Dealey a couple of days ago are going to disappear. But you've been very sloppy, David. *Very sloppy.* You left a trail of crumbs that leads right from our fall guy straight to you. And from you, it's a stone's throw to Mr. Marcello himself. That kind of sloppiness could get a man killed, if you catch my drift ..."

There's a long silence, broken only by panicked breaths.

"Hell, I know—I know," he says. "You think you got it all covered, it's always the last thing! That damn card!"

He's cracking! Time to pump him for more evidence!

"Now think, David—is there anything else we might turn up tying you to Oswald?" you say, in a friendlier tone. "Because we need to get to it before anyone else does ..."

Ferrie replies, "Well, gotta think—I mean, there might be a photo or two of us together, from back in the Civil Air Patrol days. That's years ago, now—'fore he defected."

"Anything else?" you say.

"No, no—I don't think ... AH HELL!" he replies with sudden panic, "They shot film of all us up at the camp on the Pontchartrain this summer. I said they's crazy to do that!"

You lower your voice to a grumble, "Who is 'all of us,' David? *We need to know everything.*"

You raise the tape deck headphone to your free ear, to be sure it's still recording. It is—loud and clear!

Go on to the next page.

Ferrie grows even more anxious, "The whole gang, you know? Lee, me, Guy, Veciana, the rest—OH, HELL! They even got Bishop in that, too! OH, NO! NO! *NO!*"

From the panic in his voice, it's obvious this "Bishop" character must be really important! It sounds like this film, whatever it is, is the key to cracking this case wide open! You push your bluff in the hopes that he'll give you more.

"David," you growl as menacingly as you can, "are you *really* telling me there's a film out there that ties you to Bishop *and Oswald, too?* Do you have any idea what the Attorney General will do to you if he gets his hands on—"

He doesn't even let you finish your threat. "*The ATTORNEY GENERAL?! The CIA ain't gonna leave any part of me for Bobby to FIND if that film gets out! It ties them up in this, too! YOU BOYS GOTTA GET THAT FILM! YOU GOTTA! HELL, I GOTTA GO!!*"

He slams down the phone so loud you can hear it through the wall—and now he's wailing in panic!

This is AMAZING! This "Bishop" character must be a CIA agent! And there's film of him, a Mafia pilot, and Lee Harvey Oswald all together at some camp on Lake Pontchartrain! It sounds like Angelo and Joab were both right—the assassination ties the CIA with the Mob! And you've got it all on tape! You pack up your surveillance gear as fast as you can, as Ferrie's agonized wails shake the walls. Now it's time to make your getaway!

Turn to page 168.

You lean out into the hallway to make sure the coast is clear. It is! You race down the stairs to the lobby, unable to wipe the huge smile off your face. Mission accomplished!

The lovely Italian girl is back working behind the front desk. She smiles at you in surprise. "Checking out already?"

"Yes," you smile back. "Turns out, I'm needed at home."

She checks her watch, then replies, "Well, you were only here twenty minutes. Let's just call it even, okay?"

"Wow," you reply. "That's really kind of you. Thanks."

"No problem," she says with a wink, "*Ciao*."

You turn and start walking towards the exit, but then remember you forgot to return your room key.

"Whoops!" you say, turning back. "Almost forgot!"

You reach down into your front pocket to get the key. *Ouch!*

You feel a sharp prick on your fingertip. It only takes you a second to realize, *Oh, Joab's suicide coin must've sprung its needle. Thank goodness he disarmed it!*

It only takes you another second to die.

YOU LOSE

ABOUT THE AUTHOR

JUSTIN SEWELL (born 1971) is the CEO and head writer of Despair, Inc. He is a college dropout with no meaningful achievements beyond his role in the creation of the Demotivational™ poster, surely the most trivial form of personal expression known to man other than Twitter.

He did once gain minor celebrity as an 11-year-old by stealing white phosphorus from the Fort Worth Museum of Science and History. Next time he will remember that important tip about keeping phosphorus submerged in water while transporting it, as apparently oxygen can seep into your short pockets, even if you zip them shut.

He is working on a semi-autobiographical book called *Adolescent Repair While You Wait* about his half-year experience in a Texas psychiatric hospital for teens. He'll probably never finish it.

ABOUT THE ILLUSTRATOR

PAUL STRANGER is an award-winning illustrator, painter, and matte designer living in L.A. who really shouldn't be reduced to this kind of thing. He refuses to include his real name here, because he does not want to be on any CIA, Mafia, Freemasonic or NASA hit lists.

ENDNOTES

The JFK assassination is one of the most notoriously fascinating events in American history, due both to the voluminous body of contradictory evidence presented, and the dizzying number of proposed suspects with potential motives.

This book references but a few, and often in absurd manners. But no major suspect theory presented in the book—whether plausible ('The Mafia did it!') or ludicrous ('It was an alien cover-up!')—is without a real world reference. Nor is any of the often bizarre evidence included here of our own invention.

Recognizing the potential for reader assumptions to the contrary, we've included this short overview of some of the more bizarre theories and more curious evidence referenced in this book.

1) AGENT HOSTY - It's true. Oswald really did have contact with the Dallas FBI prior to Kennedy's shooting, and made mention of the note he'd left for James Hosty days prior during an interrogation which included Hosty. Hoover was furious about it, worrying that this might suggest Oswald was an FBI informant. Many believe he actually was.

2) JOHN ABT - Officers present for Oswald's many interrogations did not record them, but did summarize some details in notes. He reportedly said, "I want that attorney in New York, Mr. Abt. I don't know him personally but I know about a case that he handled some years ago, where he represented the people who had violated the Smith Act..." Abt spent most of his career as chief counsel for the American Communist Party.

3) THE FIRST LINE-UP - Helen Markham was a key witness to the Tippit shooting, but proved profoundly unstable, producing erratic and contradictory descriptions of the suspect, and often bursting into hysteria. She was sedated with ammonia to calm her nerves. Despite the fact that Oswald was handcuffed between two suited officers, and sported bruises on his face from a recent scuffle, Markham still had difficulty identifying him as the person she saw shoot Officer Tippit.

4) DEATH THREATS - Both the Dallas Police and FBI offices received death threats the night before Oswald's transfer. Lieutenant Billy Grammer reported receiving an anonymous call he later realized was from Jack Ruby, stating, "You're going to have to make some other plans or we're going to kill Oswald right there in the basement."

5) JOHN HURT - Oswald's last attempted phone call to a John Hurt in Raleigh, N.C., was disallowed by Secret Service officers monitoring the switchboard. Of the two John Hurts living there at the time, one John D. Hurt was in military intelligence. Many believe he was a "cut-out" for a deep-cover Oswald, acting as a trusted intermediary between agents who cannot, for reasons of plausible deniability, directly communicate. Some further speculate this was an act of desperation for Oswald, who realized only too late he was being used as a patsy, and that if he was not already marked for death, a call to his cut-out surely sealed his fate.

6) TARGET PRACTICE - On November 20, 1963, two DPD officers on patrol reported seeing riflemen sighting in over the Dealey Plaza fence on silhouetted targets in an old model car in the killzone. Though noted in an FBI memo on 11/27, it wasn't disclosed to the public until it was unearthed by a 1978 Freedom of Information Act request.

7) DISINFORMATION - A common form of black propaganda employed by intelligence agencies worldwide involves the use of disinformation agents. Often, such agents gain the trust of a community by supporting a plausible conspiratorial claim. After they have become visibly associated with the group, or even a spokesperson, they proceed to unleash absurdist claims, thereby tainting the group at large in the eyes of the public. Don't knock it—it works!

8) THE LAKE PONTCHARTRAIN FILM - Perhaps no single piece of vanishing evidence had more potential to expose a possible conspiracy than the famous film reportedly unearthed in a Georgetown library by the House Select Committee on Assassinations. HSCA Deputy Chief Counsel Robert Tanenbaum claimed that the 8mm film was seen by many on the committee, and showed an illegal anti-Castro training camp set up by the CIA near Lake Pontchartrain in Louisiana. Most shockingly, participants at the camp included Mafia-friendly David Ferrie, supposed Marxist Lee Harvey Oswald, and CIA heavy David Atlee Phillips. Proof of association between Oswald and these groups would have proven more explosive than the Zapruder film itself. Its existence—and Oswald's inclusion in it—has been separately corroborated by Colonel William C. Bishop, a CIA operative involved in the "Operation 40" assassination group. Yet it mysteriously disappeared from HSCA possession before it could be released to the public. *(Thanks to you and Jenni Mudd, apparently.)*

9) DAN RATHER REPORTING - One of the only journalists permitted to see the Zapruder film in the days after the assassination was CBS up-and-comer, Dan Rather. His televised description of the details of the film are in conspicuous contradiction to the actual film itself, and give the impression that rather than reporting what he saw, he was simply following a script given to him by parties interested in propping up an "Oswald acted alone" narrative. (In other words, he may not be *entirely* reliable as a journalist...)

10) FREEMASONS - It is a widely known fact that many powerful politicians in 1960s Washington belonged to the mysterious fraternity, The Freemasons. Slightly less certain is the prospect they utilized physics-defying magic to achieve impossible rifle shots in their ceremonial "Killing of the King" ritual. *(Just FYI.)*

11) THE PRESS CONFERENCE - Jack Ruby, owner of The Carousel (Strip) Club, was known to the Dallas Police, as many officers were patrons. His presence at the DPD after the arrest of Oswald was noted by many. He impersonated a reporter to attend Henry Wade's midnight press conference, and corrected Wade on Oswald's "Fair Play for Cuba Committee" membership, despite his disavowals of personal knowledge or relationship with Oswald.

12) THE BULLET HOLE IN THE LIMOUSINE WINDSHIELD - Over a half dozen witnesses—including motorcycle patrolmen Stavis Ellis and H. R. Freeman—reported seeing a bullet hole in the front windshield of the Presidential limousine. The fact was also noted in a report dated November 27, 1963, by Secret Service Agent Charles Taylor, Jr. Eventually, photographic and film evidence surfaced confirming the matter, though it was ignored by the Warren Commission.

13) THE PARKLAND HOSPITAL STRETCHER BULLET - Known as CE399, the infamous stretcher bullet was claimed by Arlen Specter to have passed through Kennedy's back/neck and then broke a rib and shattered the wrist of Governor Connally, whereupon it lodged in Connally's thigh. The bullet then supposedly fell out onto a stretcher, in nearly pristine condition, with no traces of blood or tissue from either Kennedy or Connally. Similar bullets fired into the wrists of human cadavers for test purposes ended up mangled. *(But maybe Freemasonic magic made that possible.)*

14) ALIENS & JFK - Absurdist conspiracy theories—such as William Cooper's claim in Behold a Pale Horse that JFK was shot by the Secret Service driver of his presidential limousine—have plagued the subject of conspiratorial inquiry for years. Perhaps no claim is crazier than that of the hoax "Majestic 12" documents, which claim JFK died because he was about to reveal secret contacts between aliens and humankind. Really. We didn't make it up.

15) THE VANISHING MAUSER - Deputy Roger Craig was named the Dallas Sheriff Department's "Man of the Year" in 1960 for his role in capturing a jewel thief. Minutes after the shooting, he reportedly saw Oswald get into a green Rambler station wagon, a fact corroborated independently by a Dealey Plaza witness, Mrs. James Robinson. This was dismissed by the Warren Commission, as it implied conspiracy. Craig was also a witness to the discovery of a rifle in the Texas School Book Depository by Officers Seymour Weitzman and Eugene Boone. All agreed at the time that it was a 7.65mm German Mauser, and Weitzman, a marksman and rifle expert, filed an affidavit to that effect. Yet the casings discovered by the window were for a 6.5mm rifle. A rifle was taken into evidence which matched that size, a Mannlicher-Carcano, yet a CIA report from November 25 rejected the Carcano as the murder weapon, reiterating that the Mauser was used for the shooting. Yet a Mauser, if it had been found, disappeared from evidence. Though most witnesses to its discovery eventually changed their testimony, Craig refused. His stubbornness ultimately cost him his job. For more on this subject, watch Mark Lane's documentary "Two Men in Dallas" on Youtube.

As a footnote to the mystery of the vanishing Mauser, in 1995 the Assassination Records Review Board disclosed the discovery in the National Archives of an empty envelope from the FBI Field Office in Dallas. It had the following label: *"7.65 shell found in Dealey Plaza on 12/02/1963... determined of no value and destroyed."*

RECOMMENDED READING

*Want to learn more about the Kennedy assassination from people who **don't** believe in magic, possible alien involvement, or other kooky notions? Here are the titles we recommend most heartily.*

JFK and the Unspeakable - by James Douglass (2010)
Destiny Betrayed - by Jim DiEugenio (2012)
The Last Investigation - by Gaeton Fonzi (1993)
Breach of Trust - Gerald McKnight (2005)
The Assassinations - by Jim DiEugenio, Lisa Pease, and others (2003)

DO YOU WANT MORE "LOSE YOUR OWN ADVENTURE®" BOOKS? OF COURSE YOU DO!

Hi there, readers. So—here's the deal. *Who Killed John F. Kennedy?* cost us an absolute fortune to produce—largely due to the high costs for creating original art that recreates the cheesy, feathered-hair, gangly-body stylings of the original *Choose Your Own Adventure* book illustrations. But it's important to us to preserve that style—no parody of those wonderful old books would be complete without it!

We've already paid for the covers of our next three books—but we hope to get your help in funding the interior illustrations. To help us accelerate the production of our next *Lose Your Own Adventure®* book, *The Glass Ceiling*, we're launching a Kickstarter project on **September 4, 2013.** You'll not only have a chance to pre-order the book, sponsors will be able to buy special autographed editions, full-color poster and book bundles, or "Director's Cut" editions with even more plots and illustrations. You'll even be able to buy a part in the upcoming book as an illustrated character if you want!

To help support us (and, to be frank, save us from having egg on our faces), please visit our blog, **ThePessimist.com**, on **September 4, 2013**. Everything you'll need to know about *The Glass Ceiling* Kickstarter will be there.

Thanks for your support!

The Despair Team